WeightWatchers®

150 new and satisfying recipes helping you and your family to maintain a happier, healthier lifestyle

Kim Morphew

D0492347

delicious

SIMON & SCHUSTER
A CBS COMPANY

First published in Great Britain by
Simon & Schuster UK Ltd, 2009
A CBS Company
Copyright © 2009, Weight Watchers
International, Inc.
Simon & Schuster UK Ltd, 1st Floor,
222 Gray's Inn Road,
London WC1X 8HB
This book is copyright under the
Berne Convention.
No reproduction without permission.
All rights reserved.
13 5 7 9 10 8 6 4 2

Weight Watchers and **POINTS** are the
registered trademarks of Weight
Watchers International Inc..
Discover Plan is a trademark of Weight
Watchers International Inc., and all are
used under its control by Weight
Watchers (UK) Ltd.

Weight Watchers Publications Team
Jane Griffiths, Donna Watts,
Nina McKerlie, Nina Bhogal and
Eileen Thornton
Photography by Steve Baxter
Styling by Rachel Jukes
Food preparation and styling by
Carol Tennant
Design and typesetting by Jane Humphrey
Printed and bound in China

A CIP catalogue for this book is available
from the British Library

Pictured on the back cover: Lemon
Chicken Burger, page 101; Veggie
Sausage Ragu, page 103; Salmon and
Potato Tart, page 140; Chocolate
Marshmallow Meringue Cake, page 199
Pictured on the inside front flap: Spiced
Pear Cake, page 197
Pictured on page 4: Creamy Peppercorn
Beef, page 72
Pictured on page 5: from top to bottom,
Breakfast Rosti, page 18; Frozen
Raspberry Tiramisu, page 194

 POINTS® value logo: You'll find this easy to read **POINTS** value logo on every recipe throughout this book. The logo represents the number of **POINTS** values per serving each recipe contains. Weight Watchers **POINTS** system is a simple way to lose weight. As part of the Weight Watchers Discover Plan™ you'll enjoy eating delicious, healthy, filling foods that help keep you feeling satisfied for longer and in control of both your portion sizes and your hunger.

Filling Foods are highlighted in green – like this. Focus on these foods where you can – they keep you feeling satisfied for longer.

Y This symbol denotes a vegetarian recipe and assumes that, where relevant, free range eggs, vegetarian cheese, vegetarian virtually fat free fromage frais and vegetarian low fat crème fraîche are used. Virtually fat free fromage frais and low fat crème fraîche may contain traces of gelatine so they are not always vegetarian. Please check the labels.

❄ This symbol denotes a dish that can be frozen.

Recipe notes

Egg size Medium, unless otherwise stated.
All fruits and vegetables Medium sized unless otherwise stated.
Raw eggs Only the freshest eggs should be used. Pregnant women, the elderly and children should avoid recipes with eggs which are not fully cooked or raw.
Recipe timings These are approximate and meant to be guidelines. Please note that the preparation time includes all the steps up to and following the main cooking time(s).
Polyunsaturated margarine Use brands such as Flora Light, St Ivel Gold and Benecol Light.

contents

Welcome to *Delicious*, the new cookbook from Weight Watchers. With 150 new and satisfying recipes to choose from, you'll never be short of meal ideas that make following the Weight Watchers programme a delight. Using *Delicious* alongside the new Discover Plan™ can help to stretch your *POINTS* allowance as many of the recipes contain **Filling Foods**.

The easy to follow recipes are full of healthy, nutritious ingredients which can help you to stay satisfied for longer. And they're also great for friends and family so you won't need to prepare separate dishes to stay on track with your weight loss when cooking for others.

Whether you're looking for a filling breakfast to start your day, a satisfying lunch or delicious and nutritious suppers, you'll be spoilt for choice. You'll find over 60 vegetarian recipes to choose from and a selection of recipes that can easily be adapted for vegetarians. There's also a chapter on tasty side dishes and a fabulous dessert section too.

Each recipe has a **POINTS** value per serving clearly indicated on it, so you can easily track what you're eating and stay within your **POINTS** allowance. And the unique 'Goes Well With' and 'Goes Well After' feature makes planning complete, wholesome meals hassle-free.

We hope you enjoy the recipes in *Delicious*.

Breakfast is the most important meal of the day - so get a good start, **keep hunger at bay and boost your energy levels** with these great morning choices. Even if you only have a few minutes in the morning, you'll find something quick and delicious to enjoy every day of the week. Apple and Kiwi Crush, Café Frappe or Raspberry and Pomegranate Slurp are the perfect fast foods to keep you going well past elevenses. To start the day **feeling satisfied** for longer and for something warming as well as easy to prepare, choose from Three Oat Porridge, Griddled Fruit Salad or Nutty Bran Muffins. Nothing says 'it's the weekend - relax' like the aroma of bacon, and with Eggy Crumpets 'n' Bacon or Italian Style Poached Egg, now you can enjoy a healthy and scrumptious brunch too.

Griddled Fruit Salad, *page 12*

fluffy mushrooms

You can top or fill portabello **mushrooms** *with lots of delicious things such as* **spinach** *and* **low fat soft cheese**.

Y Serves 4

Takes *10 minutes to prepare, 20 minutes to cook*

5 *POINTS values per recipe*

79 *calories per serving*

150 g (5½ oz) low fat soft cheese

1 egg, separated

1 tablespoon finely snipped fresh chives

1 teaspoon wholegrain mustard

4 portabello mushrooms, wiped and stalk removed

6 cherry tomatoes, halved

1 spring onion, sliced finely

salt and freshly ground black pepper

1 Preheat the oven to Gas Mark 4/180°C/fan oven 160°C. In a large bowl, mix together 50 g (1¾ oz) of the soft cheese, the egg yolk, chives and wholegrain mustard. Season generously.

2 Put the mushrooms, gills side up, on a baking tray and spread each with a little of the remaining soft cheese and top each with three cherry tomato halves.

3 In another clean, grease-free bowl, whisk the egg white until it forms a stiff peak but is not dry. Then using a metal spoon, carefully fold the egg white into the egg yolk mixture. Top each mushroom with some of the cheese and egg mixture, sprinkle over the spring onions and bake in the oven for 20 minutes until golden and puffy. Serve immediately.

Serving suggestion For a more substantial brunch, serve with lots of **spinach**, sautéed in low fat cooking spray, for no additional *POINTS* values.

maple syrup granola

2 POINTS VALUE

Store this home made cereal in an airtight container so it's there whenever you need a crunchy breakfast hit. It will last for 2 weeks.

Ⓨ Makes 8
(30 g/1¼ oz) servings
Takes *5 minutes to prepare,*
15 minutes to cook
16½ *POINTS values per recipe*
137 calories *per serving*

3 Shredded Wheat, crushed roughly

25 g (1 oz) sunflower seeds

25 g (1 oz) pumpkin seeds

2 tablespoons maple syrup

15 g (½ oz) light muscovado sugar

50 g (1¾ oz) Rice Krispies

75 g (2¾ oz) ready to eat dried berries and cherries

1 Preheat the oven to Gas Mark 6/200°C/fan oven 180°C. Mix the Shredded Wheat, seeds, maple syrup and sugar in a bowl. Toss to coat and then spread out on to a baking tray. Bake in the oven for 10–15 minutes until golden, stirring halfway. Remove from the oven and leave to cool completely.

2 Break up the baked mixture and put into another bowl. Add the Rice Krispies, dried berries and cherries and mix to combine. Transfer to an airtight container.

Serving suggestion Serve with 142 ml (¼ pint) **skimmed milk**, for an additional *POINTS* value of ½ per serving.

apple and kiwi crush

The refreshing taste of kiwi will soon wake you up, and give you a good boost for the day.

Serves 2
Takes *5 minutes*
4 POINTS values per recipe
138 calories per serving

1 large eating apple, peeled, cored and chopped
1 very small banana, peeled and chopped
150 ml (5 fl oz) 100% pure pineapple juice (not from concentrate)
10 (40 g/1½ oz) white seedless grapes
2 large ripe kiwi, peeled and chopped
6 ice cubes

1 Put the apple, banana and pineapple juice into a blender, or use a hand blender, and blend until smooth. Add the grapes, kiwi and ice cubes and blend again until smooth and combined. Pour into glasses and serve immediately.

Variation Try replacing the apple and banana with 100 g (3½ oz) peeled, stoned and chopped mango and 150 g (5½ oz) peeled, de-seeded and chopped papaya for a tropical treat, and the same *POINTS* values.

café frappe

This really is breakfast in a glass. Make it the night before and chill in the fridge to save time in the morning.

Serves 1
Takes *10 minutes*
2 POINTS values per recipe
150 calories per serving

150 ml (5 fl oz) skimmed milk
2 teaspoons instant coffee
30 g (1¼ oz) non sugary Bran Flakes
4 or 5 ice cubes

1 Gently warm the skimmed milk in a small pan to a simmer. Remove from the heat and stir in the coffee granules until dissolved. Add the Bran Flakes and set aside for 2–3 minutes.

2 Put the ice cubes in a blender, or use a hand blender, and add the soaked Bran Flakes and warm coffee milk. Blend until smooth and frothy. Pour into a chunky glass or mug and serve immediately.

mandarin, banana and pineapple shake

This fruity milkshake will bring a little sunshine to your morning.

Y Serves 2
Takes *5 minutes*
3½ *POINTS values per recipe*
137 calories *per serving*

1 x 295 g can mandarin segments in natural juice, drained
1 x 227 g can pineapple pieces in natural juice, drained
1 small banana, peeled and chopped
200 ml (7 fl oz) skimmed milk
4 ice cubes

1 Put the mandarin, pineapple, banana and milk into a blender, or use a hand blender, and blend until smooth. Add the ice cubes and blend until smooth and frothy. Divide between tall glasses and serve immediately.

griddled fruit salad

Cooking pineapple, banana and orange really brings out their natural sugars, and makes this dish absolutely delicious.

Y Serves 2
Takes *15 minutes*
5 *POINTS values per recipe*
147 calories *per serving*

1 orange
3 x 50 g (1¾ oz) fresh pineapple slices, halved
1 banana, peeled and cut into thick slices on the diagonal
15 g (½ oz) fresh root ginger, peeled and sliced thinly
4 cardamom pods, seeds removed and crushed
juice of a lime
1 x 100 g pot low fat fruity fromage frais, such as peach

1 Carefully cut the top and bottom off the orange. Stand upright on a board and cut the peel and pith off in a downward motion with a serrated knife. Then cut into thick slices, collecting the juice, and put into a large bowl. Add the pineapple, banana, ginger, cardamom and lime juice. Toss gently to coat.

2 Heat a griddle pan or non stick frying pan until hot and then arrange the fruit in a single layer. You may need to do this in batches. Cook for 3–4 minutes, turning halfway through until charred and starting to caramelise. Serve in bowls, drizzled with any leftover juice from the fruit bowl, topped with the fromage frais.

nutty bran muffins

This is the perfect breakfast on the go.

 Makes 9

Takes *10 minutes to prepare, 20 minutes to cook*

22 POINTS *values per recipe*

158 calories *per serving*

75 g (2¾ oz) Bran Flakes
200 ml (7 fl oz) hot skimmed milk
150 g (5½ oz) self raising flour
1 teaspoon bicarbonate of soda
75 g (2¾ oz) ready to eat dried exotic fruits, chopped finely
2 eggs**, beaten**
50 g (1¾ oz) low fat polyunsaturated margarine, melted
15 g (½ oz) demerara sugar

1 Preheat the oven to Gas Mark 5/190°C/fan oven 170°C and line a 12 hole muffin tin with nine paper cases. Put the Bran Flakes in a bowl and pour over the hot milk. Leave to soak for 5 minutes.

2 Meanwhile, in a bowl, mix together the flour, bicarbonate of soda and chopped fruits. Stir in the eggs, melted margarine, soaked Bran Flakes and leftover milk until combined.

3 Divide between the paper cases, sprinkle over the sugar and bake for 15–20 minutes until golden and risen. Leave to cool on a wire rack.

Serving suggestion Enjoy with a latte made with 150 ml (5 fl oz) skimmed milk, for an extra ½ **POINTS** value per serving.

Variation Try using other dried fruits such as ready to eat dried apple pieces, for the same **POINTS** values per serving.

a healthy start to the day

eggs benedict rolls

*This topsy turvy version of
the brunch classic has all the
ingredients, minus the muffin,
for a real satisfying breakfast
treat.*

Serves 4
Takes *20 minutes*
11 *POINTS values per recipe*
189 *calories per serving*

4 eggs

¼ teaspoon artificial sweetener

1 tablespoon white wine vinegar

25 g (1 oz) Quark

juice of ½ a small lemon

1 tablespoon finely chopped fresh tarragon

100 ml (3½ fl oz) skimmed milk

low fat cooking spray

2 large tomatoes, sliced thinly

8 x 15 g (½ oz) Parma ham slices

30 g (1¼ oz) baby spinach leaves

salt and freshly ground black pepper

1 Fill a saucepan with 2½ cm (1 inch) cold water and bring to the boil. Meanwhile, separate two of the eggs, put the egg yolks in a medium heatproof bowl (one that fits snuggly over the saucepan) and reserve the egg whites in a jug.

2 To make the sauce, lower the heat in the saucepan to barely a simmer. Add the sweetener and vinegar to the egg yolks and place the bowl over the pan of simmering water. Using an electric whisk, whisk the egg yolks for 3–5 minutes until it is three times the original volume and very thick. Remove from the heat, season and stir in the Quark, lemon juice and tarragon. Set aside.

3 Add the remaining eggs and milk to the reserved egg whites and season. Gently whisk until beaten. Heat a non stick frying pan, spray with cooking spray and pour in a quarter of the beaten egg. Swirl the pan quickly to spread the beaten egg and make a thin pancake. Cook for 1–2 minutes until golden underneath and set on the top. Transfer to a warm plate and keep warm. Repeat to make three more egg pancakes, putting non stick baking parchment between each pancake on the warm plate.

4 To serve, spread each pancake with a little of the sauce and scatter with tomato slices, two slices of Parma ham and baby spinach leaves. Roll up like a wrap, cut in half and serve immediately.

Ⓥ **Vegetarian option** You can use a 100 g pack of **Quorn Deli Ham Style**, in place of the Parma ham, for 2 *POINTS* values per serving.

smoked salmon tarts

2½ POINTS VALUE

These pastry free tarts are delicious hot or cold. They will last in the fridge for up to 3 days and also make the perfect starter for entertaining.

Makes 6
Takes *5 minutes to prepare +
5 minutes standing, 25 minutes
to cook*
14½ POINTS *values per
recipe*
141 calories *per serving*

3 eggs
150 g (5½ oz) low fat soft cheese
1 tablespoon snipped chives
1½ tablespoons finely chopped fresh dill
zest of a large lemon
300 g (10½ oz) thin smoked salmon slices, cut into strips
50 g (1¾ oz) wild rocket, to garnish
freshly ground black pepper

1 Preheat the oven to Gas Mark 4/180°C/fan oven 160°C and line a six hole muffin tin with muffin paper cases. To make the filling, whisk together the eggs and soft cheese in a jug until smooth. Stir in the chives, dill and lemon zest and season generously with freshly ground black pepper. Set aside.

2 Line each muffin case with strips of smoked salmon, ensuring there are no gaps (it doesn't matter if the salmon sticks up above the muffin case). Pour in the filling and bake in the oven for 20–25 minutes until set and golden. Leave to stand for 5 minutes, then remove from the paper cases and serve topped with a little wild rocket.

breakfast rosti

A fantastically delicious twist on the traditional bacon and eggs. Rosti is a potato dish from Switzerland, originally eaten for breakfast. This healthy version is ideal for a lazy weekend.

Serves 4

Takes *20 minutes to prepare, 40 minutes to cook*

11½ *POINTS values per recipe*

184 calories *per serving*

low fat cooking spray

400 g (14 oz) waxy potatoes, **such as Charlotte or Désirée, scrubbed**

1 small courgette, **trimmed**

3 rashers smoked lean back bacon, **chopped finely**

2 tablespoons finely chopped fresh parsley

2 eggs, **beaten**

200 g (7 oz) cherry tomatoes **on the vine**

salt and freshly ground black pepper

1 Preheat the oven to Gas Mark 6/200°C/fan oven 180°C and spray a 1.2 litre (2 pint) ovenproof dish with cooking spray. Put the potatoes in a saucepan and cover with cold water. Bring to the boil and simmer for 5 minutes. Drain and plunge into cold water.

2 Meanwhile, coarsely grate the courgette and put in a bowl. Add the bacon, parsley and beaten eggs. Coarsely grate the parboiled potatoes and mix with the courgette mixture. Season generously and then spoon into the prepared dish. Press down with the back of a spoon, spray with the cooking spray and bake in the oven for 40 minutes.

3 Remove from the oven, top with cherry tomatoes and bake for a further 5–10 minutes until golden and tender. Cut into four and serve immediately.

Serving suggestion Enjoy with a 150 ml (5 fl oz) glass of orange juice for a satisfying Fast Start breakfast, for an extra 1 *POINTS* value per serving.

Ⓨ **Vegetarian option** You can replace the bacon with 70 g (2½ oz) Quorn Deli Bacon Style Rashers, for 2½ *POINTS* values per serving.

eggy crumpets 'n' bacon

This is ideal for a weekend breakfast.

Serves 4
Takes *20 minutes*
14½ *POINTS values per recipe*
222 *calories per serving*

2 eggs
2 tablespoons skimmed milk
1 teaspoon dried mixed herbs
4 x 46 g crumpets
200 g (7 oz) cherry tomatoes, **halved**
2 tablespoons brown sauce
2 teaspoons tomato purée
4 rashers smoked lean back bacon
low fat cooking spray
freshly ground black pepper

1 Put the eggs and milk into a jug with the dried mixed herbs and season with freshly ground black pepper. Whisk until beaten. Put the crumpets into a shallow dish and pour over the eggs. Turn to coat in the mixture and then set aside.

2 Meanwhile, put the cherry tomatoes, brown sauce, tomato purée and 4 tablespoons of cold water into a small saucepan. Gently bubble for 3–5 minutes until the tomatoes are just soft. Set aside.

3 Preheat the grill to hot. Put the bacon on a grill pan and cook for 3–5 minutes until crispy. Meanwhile, heat a non stick frying pan and spray with cooking spray. Gently cook the crumpets for 5 minutes, turning halfway, until golden and the eggs have set. Divide the crumpets between four plates and then top with crispy bacon and the tomato sauce.

Ⓨ **Vegetarian option** You can top the eggy crumpets with 50 g (1¾ oz) sliced mushrooms each, sautéed in low fat cooking spray in step 3, instead of the bacon, for 4 *POINTS* values per serving, making it perfect on Fast Start.

a yummy breakfast

three oat porridge

Brighten up your breakfast with a swirl of this yummy pear purée. It will keep in a sealable container in the fridge for 3 days.

Serves 2
Takes *10 minutes*
7 POINTS *values per recipe*
252 calories *per serving*

50 g (1¾ oz) rolled porridge oats
15 g (½ oz) fine oatmeal
25 g (1 oz) oat bran
300 ml (10 fl oz) skimmed milk
½ x 220 g can pear halves in natural juice, **drained**
25 g (1 oz) fresh raspberries
a pinch of ground cinnamon
2 tablespoons 0% fat Greek yogurt

1 Put the porridge oats, oatmeal, oat bran, skimmed milk and 150 ml (5 fl oz) cold water into a small pan and gently simmer for 4–5 minutes, stirring until the oats are tender and thickened.

2 Meanwhile, blend the pears, raspberries and cinnamon in a blender, or using a hand blender, until smooth. Spoon the porridge into bowls, mix a tablespoon of yogurt into each bowl and swirl through the pear purée. Serve immediately.

Serving suggestion Enjoy this with a latte made with 150 ml (5 fl oz) skimmed milk, for an extra ½ POINTS value per serving, and a filling Fast Start breakfast.

Tip Make double the amount of purée and store in the freezer in two 14 hole ice cube trays.

raspberry and pomegranate slurp

Just one glass of this delicious quick fix smoothie will fill you up in the morning and it makes the perfect Fast Start breakfast.

Serves 1
Takes *5 minutes*
4 POINTS *values per recipe*
260 calories *per serving*

150 ml (5 fl oz) pomegranate juice
125 g (4½ oz) fresh raspberries
1 x 150 g pot low fat raspberry yogurt
1 heaped teaspoon runny honey
a few drops of vanilla extract
4 ice cubes

1 Put the pomegranate juice and raspberries into a blender, or use a hand blender, and blend until smooth. Add the yogurt, honey, vanilla extract and ice cubes. Blend until smooth and combined. Pour into a glass and serve immediately.

Variation You can use 150 ml (5 fl oz) orange juice instead of pomegranate juice, for the same POINTS values.

Italian style poached egg

This Italian version of bacon and eggs with chorizo instead of bacon truly hits the spot. Add 1 tablespoon of white wine vinegar in step 1 before you add the egg, which can help it to coagulate.

Serves 1
Takes *15 minutes*
4½ POINTS values per recipe
263 calories per serving

1 egg
1 x 35 g slice of ciabatta
15 g (½ oz) thin chorizo slices
15 g (½ oz) reduced fat Cheddar cheese, grated
freshly ground black pepper

1 Preheat the grill to hot. Bring a large pan of water to the boil. Break the egg into a mug and set aside. Using a wooden spoon, swirl the water to create a whirlpool and then quickly and carefully lower the mug into the water and empty out the egg. Gently simmer for 3–4 minutes until opaque and cooked. Remove from the pan with a slotted spoon and drain on kitchen paper.

2 Meanwhile, put the ciabatta on a grill pan and cook for 1 minute until toasted. Remove from the grill and turn the ciabatta over to toast the other side. Add the chorizo slices to the grill pan and cook for 1 minute until the chorizo is crispy.

3 Put the ciabatta on a plate, top with the chorizo and then the poached egg. Sprinkle over the cheese and season with freshly ground black pepper. Serve immediately.

Serving suggestion Enjoy with a strong cappuccino made from 150 ml (5 fl oz) frothy **skimmed milk**, for an extra ½ **POINTS** value per serving.

Mediterranean bangers

What better way to start the day than with some fantastic, filling beans on toast? If you cover the bean mixture, it will last in the fridge for up to 3 days, making brekkie even easier.

Serves 4

Takes *10 minutes*

19 *POINTS values per recipe*

269 *calories per serving*

1 x 400 g can chopped tomatoes

1 tablespoon good quality balsamic vinegar

2 teaspoons dried oregano

1 x 410 g can cannellini beans, drained and rinsed

3 x 36 g classic frankfurters, cut into 1 cm (½ inch) lengths

4 medium slices rustic brown bread

75 g (2¾ oz) ricotta cheese

salt and freshly ground black pepper

1 Put the tomatoes, balsamic vinegar, oregano, cannellini beans and frankfurters into a small pan. Gently simmer for 2–3 minutes until heated through. Season to taste.

2 Meanwhile, toast the bread and then put a slice on each plate. Top each slice with a quarter of the bean mixture and a quarter of the ricotta. Serve immediately.

Ⓥ **Vegetarian option** You can replace the frankfurters with three Quorn sausages, cut into thick slices, for a *POINTS* value of 4 per serving.

relax into the weekend

You can look forward to **a satisfying lunch** with this fantastic combination of light lunches, soups and snacks. It's all the inspiration you'll need to stay one step ahead of hunger, whether it's at home, at work or on the go. Sometimes life is so busy, even grabbing a sandwich can be tricky, but with a little bit of planning the Herbed Goat's Cheese Pâté or Figs in Blankets can be the ideal solution. Nothing is more satisfying than Watercress and Asparagus Soup or Chilled Tomato Soup and they both have **zero *POINTS* values** so they're sure to **brighten up your day**. Transform lunchtimes with the easily portable Beany Beef, The Ultimate Ham Salad or Antipasto Frittata and take that extra 5 minutes to sit down and enjoy.

Fresh Salmon Salad, *page 39*

chilled tomato soup

Y ❄ *soup only*
Serves 4
Takes *10 minutes*
0 POINTS *values per recipe*
58 calories *per serving*

goes well with...

The Wild Rocket and Spinach Pesto on page 166, in place of the tomato salsa, for an extra ½ POINTS value per serving.

1 kg (2 lb 4 oz) very ripe tomatoes on the vine, halved
100 g (3½ oz) cucumber, de-seeded and diced finely
½ red pepper, de-seeded and diced finely
1 tablespoon finely chopped fresh flat leaf parsley
1 tablespoon finely chopped fresh basil
75 g (2¾ oz) yellow or red cherry tomatoes, halved
celery salt
freshly ground black pepper
to serve
a few drops of Tabasco
12 ice cubes

1 Put the vine tomatoes into a food processor, or use a hand blender, and blend until puréed. You may need to do this in batches. Put a large, extra fine sieve over a bowl and pour in the pulped tomato. Allow the juice to drain through the sieve, leaving the seeds and skin in the sieve and then discard.

2 To make the salsa, in a small bowl, mix together the cucumber, pepper, parsley, basil and cherry tomatoes. Season with celery salt and freshly ground black pepper. Serve the soup in bowls with spoonfuls of the tomato salsa, Tabasco and three ice cubes per bowl.

Serving suggestion Great on a hot summer's day when served with 2 x 15 g (½ oz) wholewheat crispbreads per person, for an additional 2 **POINTS** values per serving.

bursting with flavour

watercress and asparagus soup

This smooth, velvety soup is very refreshing in the summer and wonderfully comforting on a winter's day.

Ⓥ Serves 4
Takes *25 minutes*
0 POINTS *values per recipe*
42 calories *per serving*

900 ml (1½ pints) vegetable stock
1 baby cauliflower, trimmed and chopped roughly
350 g (12 oz) asparagus spears, trimmed and chopped
4 spring onions, trimmed and chopped
50 g (1¾ oz) watercress
1 x 25 g pack fresh mint, leaves only
salt and freshly ground black pepper

1 Put the stock and cauliflower in a large pan and bring to the boil. Add the asparagus and spring onions, bring back to the boil and simmer for 3 minutes. Take off the heat and stir in the watercress and mint until wilted. Leave to cool for 5–10 minutes.

2 Carefully blend the soup in a blender, or using a hand blender, until smooth. Gently reheat if necessary, check the seasoning and serve immediately in warmed bowls.

Serving suggestion Serve with 2 x 15 g (½ oz) wholewheat cripsbreads and 1 tablespoon of 0% fat Greek yogurt per person, for an extra 2½ **POINTS** values per serving.

the ultimate ham salad

Great for a packed lunch or picnic, but keep the soft cheese in a separate tub until ready to eat.

Serves 2
Takes 10 minutes
3½ POINTS values per recipe
113 calories per serving

1 orange
1 small carrot, trimmed, peeled and grated
50 g (1¾ oz) wild rocket
½ red onion, sliced finely
½ teaspoon cumin seeds, crushed lightly
30 g (1¼ oz) baby pickled gherkins, drained and sliced
75 g (2¾ oz) wafer thin ham
2 tablespoons low fat soft cheese

1 Carefully cut the top and bottom off the orange. Stand upright on a board and cut the peel and pith off in a downward motion. Then cut into segments, between the membrane, collecting any juice, and put into a large bowl. Add the carrot and wild rocket and toss to coat.
2 Arrange the orange mixture on a plate and scatter over the onion, cumin seeds and gherkins. Top with folds of wafer thin ham and the soft cheese. Serve immediately.

antipasto frittata

Here are all the flavours of sunny Italy, wrapped up in a tasty wedge.

Serves 4

Takes *20 minutes to prepare + 10 minutes standing*

7½ POINTS *values per recipe*

146 calories *per serving*

4 eggs

50 ml (2 fl oz) skimmed milk

1 tablespoon dried mixed herbs

60 g (2 oz) roasted red peppers in brine, drained, de-seeded and sliced

25 g (1 oz) sliced black olives in brine, drained

1 x 400 g can artichoke hearts in brine, drained and halved

150 g (5½ oz) cooked new potatoes, sliced thinly

low fat cooking spray

salt and freshly ground black pepper

1 Preheat the grill to medium. Whisk together the eggs, skimmed milk, dried herbs and seasoning in a large bowl. Add the peppers, olives, artichoke hearts and potatoes, stirring until coated.

2 Heat a small, deep non stick frying pan, ideally with a metal handle, spray with cooking spray and pour in the eggs and vegetables. Using a spatula, flatten the top, distributing the vegetables. Gently cook for 5–6 minutes until golden underneath, then transfer to the preheated grill and cook for 3–4 minutes until golden and just set. Put a cloth on the handle to remove the pan. Leave to stand for 5–10 minutes, then cut into four and serve.

Tip If you don't have a metal handle on your frying pan, place the pan just far enough under the grill to cook the frittata.

smoked chicken salad

*If you can't find this delicious smoked and herb-infused chicken, then leftover roast chicken will work just as well, for the same **POINTS** values.*

Serves 2

Takes *10 minutes*

6 POINTS *values per recipe*

184 calories *per serving*

goes well with...

the Spiced Pear Cake on page 197, for an extra 3 POINTS values per serving.

½ small Batavia or curly lettuce, leaves separated

100 g (3½ oz) cucumber, halved and sliced thinly on the diagonal

150 g (5½ oz) cherry tomatoes, halved

½ yellow pepper, de-seeded and sliced into rings

1 tablespoon French mustard

2 teaspoons light soy sauce

2 teaspoons runny honey

1 tablespoon white wine vinegar

1 x 100 g pack cooked sliced smoked chicken

25 g (1 oz) croûtons

salt and freshly ground black pepper

1 Put the lettuce, cucumber, tomatoes and pepper into a salad bowl. In a jug, whisk together the mustard, soy sauce, honey and vinegar until smooth and season.

2 Divide the salad between two plates and top with folds of chicken and croûtons. Drizzle over the dressing and serve immediately.

figs in blankets

To make this lunch, make sure you use plump and juicy ripe figs. However, two ripe, peeled and cored dessert pears, such as a rocha, will also work well, for 3½ POINTS values per serving.

Serves 2
Takes *10 minutes*
6 POINTS *values per recipe*
184 calories *per serving*

goes well with...
the Nutty Bran Muffins on page 15, for an extra 2½ POINTS values per serving.

½ x 125 g bag mixed salad leaves, **such as lamb's lettuce, verdina and spinach**
25 g (1 oz) sun dried tomatoes, sliced roughly
½ red onion, **sliced finely**
4 x 30 g (1¼ oz) thinly sliced roast ham
75 g (2¾ oz) low fat soft cheese
2 ripe figs, **cut in half**
2 tablespoons snipped fresh cress, **such as purple radish or mustard**
for the dressing
30 g (1¼ oz) onion marmalade or chutney
1 teaspoon wholegrain mustard
1 tablespoon sherry vinegar
1 tablespoon boiling water
salt and freshly ground black pepper

1 To make the dressing, mix together the onion marmalade or chutney, mustard, sherry vinegar and the boiling water in a jug. Season and set aside to cool.

2 Meanwhile, put the salad leaves, sun dried tomatoes and onion in a bowl. Add half the dressing and gently toss to coat. Divide between two plates.

3 Lay a slice of ham on a board and put a teaspoon of soft cheese in the middle. Season with freshly ground black pepper and top with half a fig. Wrap the fig up in the ham. Repeat with all fig halves. Divide them between the plates, scatter over the cress and drizzle with the remaining dressing. Serve immediately.

Serving suggestion Serve with a 30 g (1¼ oz) slice of French baguette per person, for an extra 1½ **POINTS** values per serving

herbed goat's cheese pâté

This will last for up to 3 days, covered in the fridge. It would also make a great dinner party starter, spooned into small ramekins to make individual portions.

Ⓥ Serves 4

Takes *5 minutes to prepare, 1 hour to chill*

14 POINTS *values per recipe*

149 calories *per serving*

goes well with...

the Spring Onion and Cheddar Tray Bread on page 178, for an extra 2½ POINTS values per serving.

150 g (5½ oz) medium fat French soft goat's cheese
1 tablespoon finely chopped fresh parsley
½ tablespoon finely chopped fresh dill
½ teaspoon garlic purée
3 tablespoons low fat fromage frais
zest of ½ a lemon
15 g (½ oz) small capers **in sherry vinegar, drained**
50 g (1¾ oz) reduced fat mature Cheddar cheese, grated
freshly ground black pepper
2 tablespoons snipped fresh chives, **to garnish**

1 In a bowl, mix together the goat's cheese, parsley, dill, garlic purée, fromage frais, lemon zest, capers and Cheddar cheese until combined. Season with freshly ground black pepper and spoon into a 300 ml (10 fl oz) dish. Sprinkle over the chives and gently press down with the back of a spoon.

2 Chill for 1 hour and then serve when needed.

Serving suggestion Serve with chicory leaves and six melba toast per person, for an extra 1 **POINTS** value per serving.

beany beef

If you prepare this the night before for a packed lunch, don't mix the lettuce and cress through until the morning.

Serves 2

Takes *5 minutes*

8 POINTS *values per recipe*

195 calories *per serving*

1 teaspoon Dijon mustard
1 teaspoon wholegrain mustard
50 g (1¾ oz) low fat fromage frais
30 g (1¼ oz) low fat soft cheese with garlic and herbs
1 x 410 g can cannellini beans, **drained and rinsed**
50 g (1¾ oz) roasted red pepper, **drained, de-seeded and diced**
1 Little Gem lettuce, **shredded finely**
2 tablespoons snipped fresh salad cress
75 g (2¾ oz) sliced roast beef
freshly ground black pepper

1 In a bowl, mix together both mustards, fromage frais, soft cheese and freshly ground black pepper.

2 Add the cannellini beans, pepper, lettuce and cress and gently fold to combine. Spoon between two plates and top with folds of the sliced beef.

Ⓥ Vegetarian option You can replace the beef with chargrilled slices of aubergine and courgette, for 2½ **POINTS** values per serving.

puffy pancetta and leek omelette

4 POINTS VALUE

Pancetta is Italian dry cured bacon, and you can use 75 g (2¾ oz) diced **lean back bacon** instead, for 3½ *POINTS* values per serving.

Serves 4
Takes *20 minutes*
15 POINTS values per recipe
174 calories *per serving*

goes well with...

the Tray Bake Date Scones on page 195, for an extra 2½ POINTS values per serving.

3 eggs, **separated**
75 g (2¾ oz) ricotta cheese
2 tablespoons finely chopped fresh parsley
75 g (2¾ oz) pancetta, diced

1 leek, sliced finely and rinsed
75 g (2¾ oz) frozen peas, defrosted
low fat cooking spray
salt and freshly ground black pepper

1 In a large bowl, mix together the egg yolks, 50 g (1¾ oz) ricotta, parsley and seasoning. Set aside. Heat a deep non stick frying pan, about 18 cm (7 inches), and cook the pancetta for 1–2 minutes until crispy. Remove and drain on kitchen paper. Add the leek to the pan and cook for 3–4 minutes until softened but not coloured. Remove and set aside.

2 In a clean, grease-free bowl, whisk the egg whites until nearly stiff peaks. Using a metal spoon, carefully fold the egg whites into the ricotta mixture along with half of each of the crispy pancetta, leeks and peas until combined.

3 Preheat the grill to medium. Reheat the frying pan and spray with cooking spray. Pour in the egg mixture and gently cook for 3–4 minutes until golden underneath. While still on the heat, top the omelette with the remaining ricotta, pancetta, leeks and peas. Transfer to the grill and cook for 3–4 minutes until golden and puffy. Serve immediately in wedges.

fresh salmon salad

Pea shoots *are young, tender tips of garden peas that have a distinctive 'pea' flavour, making them the perfect salad leaf. But if you can't find them, then* lamb's lettuce *is a great alternative.*

Serves 2

Takes *5 minutes*

9½ POINTS *values per recipe*

243 calories *per serving*

goes well with...

The Mandarin, Banana and Pineapple Shake on page 12, for an extra 2 POINTS values per serving.

1 small courgette, **trimmed and grated**

1 avocado, **peeled, stoned and cut into thick slices**

zest and juice of a small lemon

75 g (2¾ oz) low fat fromage frais

1 teaspoon mint sauce

75 g (2¾ oz) cucumber, **de-seeded and diced finely**

1 x 50 g bag pea shoots

100 g (3½ oz) smoked salmon

freshly ground black pepper

1 Mix together the courgette, avocado, lemon zest and juice in a bowl and season with freshly ground black pepper. Set aside. In a small bowl, mix together the fromage frais, mint sauce, cucumber. Season with freshly ground black pepper.

2 Divide the pea shoots between two plates and scatter over the courgette and avocado mixture. Top with folds of smoked salmon and a generous dollop of the cucumber mixture. Serve immediately.

Indian spiced millet

Similar to couscous and bulgur wheat, millet grain is a very versatile cereal. It's available at most supermarkets or health food shops but if you can't find it, use the same amount of bulgur wheat, for the same POINTS values per serving.

Serves 2
Takes *10 minutes to prepare,*
15 minutes to cook
9 POINTS *values per recipe*
215 calories *per serving*

100 g (3½ oz) dried millet grain
300 ml (10 fl oz) hot chicken stock
4 freeze dried curry leaves
1 egg
1 small red onion, chopped finely
1 small red chilli, de-seeded and sliced finely
2 teaspoons black or yellow mustard seeds
1 teaspoon garam masala
50 g (1¾ oz) baby spinach leaves, shredded roughly
100 g (3½ oz) cooked lean skinless chicken, cut into bite size slices

1 Put the millet grain in a lidded saucepan with the hot chicken stock and curry leaves. Bring to the boil, cover and simmer for 12–15 minutes until tender and all the stock has been absorbed. Meanwhile, put the egg in a small pan and cover with cold water. Bring to the boil and then simmer for 5–6 minutes. Drain and plunge into cold water.

2 Transfer the millet grain to a bowl and stir in the onion, chilli, mustard seeds, garam masala, spinach and chicken. Divide the salad between two plates.

3 Peel the egg, cut in half and put on top of each salad. Serve immediately.

feta stack salad

This scrummy lunch is sweet, salty, crunchy and soft, making it totally mouthwatering.

Ⓥ Serves 1
Takes *5 minutes*
4½ POINTS *values per recipe*
319 calories *per serving*

juice of ½ an orange
2 teaspoons toasted walnut oil
15 g (½ oz) stem ginger in syrup, drained and chopped finely
60 g (2 oz) reduced fat feta cheese, cut into thin slices
¼ x 150 g bag herb salad leaves
1 celery stick, sliced finely
1 small carrot, trimmed, peeled and grated
50 g (1¾ oz) crinkle cut pickled beetroot slices, drained
1 teaspoon golden linseeds
freshly ground black pepper

1 In a shallow bowl, mix together the orange juice, oil and ginger. Season generously with freshly ground black pepper, add the sliced feta and toss to coat.

2 Put the salad leaves on to a plate and scatter over the celery and carrot. Top with a few slices of beetroot, then the feta and repeat the layers until both are used up. Drizzle over any remaining dressing, sprinkle with linseeds and serve immediately.

bagel trout salad

Bagels are delicious with these tasty, fresh flavours.

Serves 1
Takes *20 minutes*
5 POINTS *values per recipe*
352 calories *per serving*

28 g (1¼ oz) mini bagel, sliced in half, then each half sliced into three pieces

low fat cooking spray

75 g (2¾ oz) cucumber

25 g (1 oz) wild rocket

1 tablespoon of less than 3% fat French dressing

25 g (1 oz) low fat soft cheese

zest and juice of ½ a lemon

½ small red onion, sliced finely

15 g (½ oz) small capers in sherry vinegar, drained

¼ ripe avocado, peeled, stoned and cut into moons

2 small tomatoes on the vine, cut into wedges

75 g (2¾ oz) lightly smoked trout, flaked into large pieces

salt and freshly ground black pepper

1 Preheat the oven to Gas Mark 5/190°C/fan oven 170°C. Spray the bagel pieces with cooking spray and arrange on a baking tray. Bake for 8–10 minutes until golden and crispy.

2 Meanwhile, using a potato peeler and starting on one side, cut the cucumber into ribbons, stopping when you get to the seeds. Then start on another side and continue until all that is left is a column of seeds. Discard the seeds and put the ribbons in a bowl along with the rocket. Add the French dressing and gently toss to coat. Transfer on to a plate.

3 In a small bowl, mix together the soft cheese, lemon zest and juice and season. Set aside. Scatter the bagel pieces, onion, capers, avocado and tomatoes over the rocket salad and top with the flaked trout and a dollop of the cheese mixture.

crunchy parmesan chicken

Finger lickin' good. These golden nuggets are scrummy.

❄ raw only
Serves 2
Takes *10 minutes to prepare,*
15 minutes to cook
10 *POINTS values per recipe*
313 calories *per serving*

goes well with...

**1 tablespoon of Wasabi,
Lime and Mayo Dressing,
on page 172, to dip into,
for an extra 1½ POINTS
values per serving.**

25 g (1 oz) dried polenta
1 teaspoon mustard powder
25 g (1 oz) Parmesan cheese, grated
1 egg, beaten
2 x 150 g (5½ oz) skinless boneless chicken breasts, **cut into even,**
   bite size chunks
freshly ground black pepper

1 Preheat the oven to Gas Mark 6/200°C/fan oven 180°C and put a non stick baking
   tray in to heat. Mix together the polenta, mustard powder, Parmesan and freshly
   ground black pepper and put into a bowl. Put the beaten egg into another bowl.

2 Put the chicken chunks first in the beaten egg to coat and then spoon into the
   cheese mixture. Stir until all the pieces are coated. You can be quite rough.
   Remove the baking tray from the oven, transfer the chicken to the tray and bake
   for 15 minutes until golden and cooked. Serve immediately.

Serving suggestion Especially good with a large salad of **Little Gem leaves**,
tomatoes, **cucumber**, **peppers** and **radishes**, for no additional **POINTS** values.

crabayo bruschetta

If you're on the move, cook
the ciabatta and wrap it in foil.
Spoon the crab mixture into a
sealable container and then
serve when needed.

Serves 2
Takes *15 minutes*
10 *POINTS values per recipe*
293 calories *per serving*

1 x 170 g can white crab meat in brine, drained
2 tablespoons reduced fat mayonnaise
zest and juice of ½ a lime
1 tablespoon finely chopped fresh coriander
a generous pinch of dried chilli flakes
1 small ciabatta (150 g/5½ oz), cut in half lengthways
low fat cooking spray
freshly ground black pepper
to serve
50 g (1¾ oz) cucumber, de-seeded and sliced finely
2 spring onions, trimmed and shredded

1 Mix together the crab meat, mayonnaise, lime zest and juice, coriander, chilli flakes and freshly ground black pepper in a bowl. Set aside.

2 Cut each of the ciabatta halves in half again and spray with cooking spray. Heat a griddle pan or non stick frying pan until hot and cook the ciabatta slices for 3–4 minutes until charred, then turn over and cook for a further 3–4 minutes. Remove from the pan and then top each with the crab mixture. Top with the cucumber and spring onions and serve immediately.

Serving suggestion For an easy lunch, use half the crab mixture to fill two medium slices of wholemeal bread, for 4½ **POINTS** values per serving.

Variation Why not try mixing a drained 200 g can of tuna steak in brine, instead of the crab, for the same **POINTS** values?

If you are looking for great value for your **POINTS** allowance, as well as some new and inspiring ways with poultry, you'll love this wonderful chapter of recipes. Try the Spicy Chicken Laksa, Tangy Duck and Plum Stir Fry or how about Paprika Chicken or Turkey Salsa Tagliatelle? They're all delicious as well as nutritious. For something quick, turn to Crunchy Fruity Salad or Leftover Chicken Salad - and you'll be sitting down at the table in minutes. All in One Roast or Spicy Barley Chicken are perfect for one pot cooking and make mealtimes so much easier, with less washing up afterwards. With their wonderfully intense flavours, these satisfying curries, stir-fries and bakes, are sure to become firm favourites.

Spiced Chicken Parcels, *page 54*

leftover chicken salad

You'll never be stuck again for what to do with leftover roast chicken.

Serves 1
Takes *10 minutes*
2 *POINTS* *values per recipe*
201 calories *per serving*

50 g (1¾ oz) cooked skinless chicken, **shredded**
25 g (1 oz) low fat soft cheese with garlic and herbs
25 g (1 oz) 0% fat Greek yogurt
1 teaspoon wholegrain mustard
1 tablespoon chopped fresh flat leaf parsley
½ x 400 g can artichoke hearts **in brine, drained and quartered**
25 g (1 oz) mild or hot pepperdew peppers, **drained and sliced**
60 g (2 oz) cucumber, **diced**
¼ x 137 g bag spinach, watercress and rocket salad
salt and freshly ground black pepper

1 In a bowl, mix together the chicken, soft cheese, yogurt, mustard and parsley and season. Gently fold through the artichoke hearts, peppers and cucumber.
2 Put the salad leaves on to a plate and top with the creamy chicken mixture. Serve immediately.

incredibly tasty
and satisfying

fragrant chicken curry

You can use a 250 g pack of *tofu*, diced, instead of the chicken, for 1 **POINTS** value per serving, for a vegetarian option.

❋ Serves 4

Takes *20 minutes to prepare, 10 minutes to cook*

11 *POINTS* values per recipe

228 calories *per serving*

low fat cooking spray

600 g (1 lb 5 oz) skinless boneless chicken breasts, cut into bite size chunks

1 red pepper, de-seeded and sliced finely

30 g (1¼ oz) fresh ginger, peeled and grated

2 garlic cloves, crushed

2 freeze dried lime leaves

1 teaspoon mild or hot chilli powder

1 tablespoon mild curry powder

50 g (1¾ oz) low fat soft cheese

1 x 400 g can chopped tomatoes with herbs

150 ml (5 fl oz) chicken stock

75 g (2¾ oz) mange tout, shredded finely lengthways, to serve

1 Heat a deep non stick saucepan and spray with the cooking spray. Add the chicken chunks and cook for 5 minutes until brown all over. You may need to do this in batches. Remove and set aside.

2 Spray the pan again and add the pepper, ginger, garlic and lime leaves. Cook for 1 minute. Stir in the chilli powder, curry powder and return the chicken to the pan, stirring constantly for 1 minute.

3 Add the soft cheese, tomatoes and stock. Bring to the boil and simmer gently for 10 minutes until thickened and chicken is cooked. Serve immediately topped with the shredded mange tout.

chilli crispy goujons

This is even faster than a Chinese take away.

Serves 2
Takes *15 minutes*
7 POINTS *values per recipe*
269 calories *per serving*

350 g (12 oz) skinless boneless chicken breasts, **cut into thin strips**
2 teaspoons cornflour
2 tablespoons soy sauce
low fat cooking spray

3 tablespoons sweet chilli sauce
½ teaspoon Thai fish sauce
2 sprigs of fresh mint, **leaves only**
½ x 25 g pack fresh coriander, **leaves only**
1 lime, halved, to serve

1 Mix together the chicken strips and cornflour in a bowl. Add the soy sauce and continue to mix until coated. Heat a non stick frying pan until hot and spray with the cooking spray. Add the chicken, and cook for 5–6 minutes, turning until brown all over. You may have to do this in batches.

2 Meanwhile, mix together the chilli sauce, 2 tablespoons of cold water and fish sauce. Return all the chicken to the pan, pour the sauce over the chicken and cook for a further 2 minutes until cooked and starting to caramelize. Toss through the mint and coriander and serve immediately with the lime halves.

Serving suggestion Serve with 150 g (5½ oz) cooked **brown rice** per person and a mixed zero **POINTS** value **salad**, for an extra 3 **POINTS** values per serving.

zingy duck salad

Tender chunks of duck coated in coriander, Thai 7 spice and teriyaki top this fruity salad. Delicious hot or cold.

Serves 2
Takes *20 minutes*
8 POINTS *values per recipe*
241 calories *per serving*

2 x 150 g (5½ oz) skinless duck breasts, **cut into small cubes**
½ teaspoon coriander seeds, crushed
½ teaspoon Thai 7 spice
1 tablespoon teriyaki sauce
low fat cooking spray
½ x 150 g bag bistro salad leaves

100 g (3½ oz) cucumber, **diced**
1 large red chilli, **de-seeded and sliced finely**
½ pomegranate, **seeds removed and reserved**
zest of a lime
2 tablespoons 0% fat Greek **yogurt**

1 Mix together the duck, coriander seeds, Thai 7 spice and teriyaki sauce in a bowl. Heat a non stick frying pan and spray with the cooking spray. Cook the duck for 5–10 minutes until cooked to your liking, turning occasionally. Transfer to a plate, cover loosely with foil and set aside.

2 Divide the salad leaves between two plates and scatter over the cucumber, chilli and pomegranate seeds. Mix together the lime zest and Greek yoghurt. Top each salad with half the duck cubes and a dollop of yogurt. Serve immediately.

Tip To remove the seeds from a pomegranate, firmly roll the fruit between your hands, then cut it in half and empty the seeds in a bowl.

tangy duck and plum stir fry

*Curly leaf kale works really well in this stir fry but you can use any type of green such as **spinach** or **Savoy cabbage**. Look out for bags of baby leaf greens that are bursting with flavour.*

Serves 2
Takes *20 minutes*
8½ POINTS *values per recipe*
344 calories *per serving*

1 x 200 g pack skinless boneless mini duck fillets
low fat cooking spray
2 garlic cloves, sliced
1 small red chilli, sliced finely
1 red onion, cut into thin wedges
100 g (3½ oz) small broccoli florets, cut in half if large

50 g (1¾ oz) curly leaf kale, chopped
50 g (1¾ oz) beansprouts
2 tablespoons sake (Japanese rice wine), optional
100 g (3½ oz) plum sauce
juice of an orange

1 Heat a wok or non stick frying pan until very hot. Spray the duck fillets with the cooking spray and cook for 2 minutes, stirring until starting to brown. Add the garlic, chilli, onion and broccoli and continue to stir fry for 3 minutes.

2 Stir in the curly leaf kale and beansprouts and continue to cook for 5 minutes until wilted and tender. Add the sake, if using, and bubble for a few seconds then stir in the plum sauce, orange juice and 3 tablespoons of cold water. Literally bubble for about 1 minute until thickened slightly. Serve immediately.

Serving suggestion Serve with 50 g (1¾ oz) dried **egg noodles** per person, cooked according to the packet instructions, for an additional 2½ **POINTS** values per serving.

spicy barley chicken

Originally from the Middle East, pearl barley is a husked and polished grain, with an almost nutty flavour. You can find it in most supermarkets near the lentils and other grains.

Serves 6
Takes *20 minutes to prepare, 1 hour 5 minutes to cook*
26½ *POINTS values per recipe*
318 calories *per serving*

goes well with...
The Sparkling Fruit Jelly on page 192, for an additional 2 *POINTS* **values per serving.**

6 x 165 g (5¾ oz) skinless
   boneless chicken breasts,
   each cut into 3 pieces on the
   diagonal
low fat cooking spray
1 onion, **chopped roughly**
2 garlic cloves, **chopped**
1 teaspoon ground turmeric
1 teaspoon ground cumin

1 teaspoon ground coriander
200 g (7 oz) dried pearl barley
600 ml (1 pint) chicken stock
150 g (5½ oz) cherry tomatoes,
   halved
1 x 25 g pack fresh coriander,
   leaves chopped
salt and freshly ground black
   pepper

1   Heat a non stick lidded saucepan and spray the chicken with the cooking spray. Cook the chicken pieces for 5 minutes until brown. You may need to do this in batches. Return the chicken to the pan. Add the onion and garlic and cook for 3–4 minutes until starting to soften.

2   Add the turmeric, cumin and ground coriander and cook for 1 minute, stirring. Add the pearl barley and chicken stock. Bring to the boil. Cover and simmer for 1 hour until the juices have nearly all been absorbed and the barley is tender. Stir through the tomatoes and half the coriander and cook for 3–4 minutes until just soft. Check the seasoning and then top with the remaining coriander and serve immediately in bowls.

crunchy fruity salad

Quince cheese (also known as membrillo) is not actually cheese; it's a fruit spread with a tangy pear and apple flavour. It is found in most large supermarkets, either at the deli or the cheese counter or in the special selection row.

Serves 2
Takes 10 minutes
9 POINTS values per recipe
289 calories per serving

1 large chicory bulb, cut into eighths
1 Little Gem lettuce, sliced
25 g (1 oz) walnut halves, chopped roughly
100 g (3½ oz) cooked sliced skinless chicken
2 celery sticks, trimmed and sliced finely
2 spring onions, sliced finely
1 small red apple, cored and sliced thinly
25 g (1 oz) membrillo or quince cheese
2 teaspoons red wine vinegar
1 tablespoon extra virgin olive oil
salt and freshly ground black pepper

1 Separate the chicory and Little Gem leaves and put into a salad bowl. Scatter over the walnut pieces, chicken, celery, spring onions and apple slices.

2 In a small jug, mix together the quince cheese, vinegar, olive oil and 2 tablespoons of cold water. Season and drizzle over the salad. Serve immediately.

Ⓥ Vegetarian option You can use a 100 g pack of Quorn Deli Ham Style in place of the chicken, for 4 POINTS values per serving.

fresh and flavoursome

spiced chicken parcels

The chicken steams in these little packages, making it really juicy.

Serves 4

Takes *10 minutes to prepare, 40 minutes to cook*

18 *POINTS values per recipe*

265 calories *per serving*

goes well with...

The Stir Fried Greens on page 166, for an extra ½ POINTS value per serving.

30 g (1¼ oz) low fat polyunsaturated margarine

2 large carrots, peeled and cut into batons

4 x 165 g (5¾ oz) skinless boneless chicken breasts

2 tablespoons runny honey

2 garlic cloves, sliced

4 star anise

2 cinnamon sticks, broken in half

8 cardamon pods, split

150 ml (5 fl oz) dry white wine

1 Preheat the oven to Gas Mark 4/180°C/fan oven 160°C. Arrange four pieces of foil, measuring 30 cm x 30 cm (12 inches x 12 inches), on a clean surface. Divide the margarine and carrot sticks between the foil squares, putting them in the centre of each square and top each with a chicken breast.

2 Drizzle each chicken breast with half a tablespoon of honey and then scatter over half a garlic clove, 1 star anise, half a cinnamon stick and two cardamon pods. Fold up the sides of each foil square to make a parcel, leaving an opening in the top. Pour a quarter of the wine into each parcel and then seal completely.

3 Put on a baking tray and bake in the oven for 40 minutes until cooked. To serve, open the parcels, discard the spices and serve each with the carrots and the juices drizzled over.

Serving suggestion Add 150 g (5½ oz) diced **potatoes** per person, sautéed in low fat cooking spray until golden and crispy, for an additional 1½ *POINTS* values per serving.

Oriental chicken

Sushi nori is paper thin toasted sheets of seaweed and is available from most supermarkets or Oriental shops. It is usually used in Japanese cooking for wrapping sushi.

Serves 4
Takes *15 minutes to prepare, 25 minutes to cook*
18½ POINTS *values per recipe*
348 calories *per serving*

150 g (5½ oz) dried brown basmati rice
2 x 5 g sushi nori seaweed sheets, torn into large pieces
2 teaspoons Chinese 5 spice powder
4 x 165 g (5¾ oz) skinless boneless chicken breasts
low fat cooking spray
8 radishes, trimmed and grated
50 g (1¾ oz) beansprouts
1 small Chinese leaf, trimmed and shredded finely
1 x 25 g pack fresh coriander, leaves chopped
1 tablespoon sushi rice seasoning
juice of a lime

1 Preheat the oven to Gas Mark 4/180°C/fan oven 160°C. Put the rice into a lidded saucepan and cover with boiling water. Bring back to the boil and simmer for 20–25 minutes until tender.

2 Meanwhile, in a small food processor, whizz the seaweed and Chinese 5 spice powder until it's chopped roughly. Transfer to a shallow bowl and roll each chicken breast in the mixture to coat.

3 Transfer the chicken breasts to a non stick baking tray, spray with the cooking spray and bake in the oven for 20–25 minutes until cooked and juices run clear. Remove from the oven, loosely cover with foil and set aside for 5 minutes.

4 Meanwhile, in a large salad bowl mix together the radishes, beansprouts, Chinese leaf, coriander, sushi rice seasoning and lime juice. Drain the rice, stir into the salad bowl until combined and then divide between four plates. Slice the chicken into thick slices on the diagonal and serve on top of each rice salad.

turkey chicory bake

Chicory is also known as Belgian Endive and is available in yellow or red varieties.

Serves 4

Takes *15 minutes to prepare, 45 minutes to cook*

20 POINTS *values per recipe*

301 calories *per serving*

low fat cooking spray

1 small red onion**, chopped finely**

500 g (1 lb 2 oz) lean turkey mince

1 x 200 g pack low fat soft cheese with garlic and herbs

50 ml (2 fl oz) chicken stock

2 small chicory bulbs**, trimmed and sliced thickly**

350 g (12 oz) Charlotte potatoes**, peeled and cut into thin wedges lengthways**

1 Preheat the oven to Gas Mark 6/200°C/fan oven 180°C. Heat a non stick frying pan and spray with the cooking spray. Add the onion and cook for 3 minutes until softened but not brown. Add the mince and cook for 5 minutes until brown, breaking up with a wooden spoon.

2 Remove from the heat and stir in the soft cheese and chicken stock until smooth. Stir in the chicory and spoon into a 1.2 litre (2 pint) ovenproof dish. Top with the potato wedges, spray with the cooking spray and bake in the oven for 45 minutes until golden and cooked. Serve immediately.

Serving suggestion Serve with a generous mixed salad of tomatoes, cucumber, peppers and herb salad leaves, for no additional **POINTS** values.

Ⓨ **Vegetarian option** You can use a 350 g pack of Quorn Chicken Style Pieces instead of the turkey mince, for 3½ **POINTS** values per serving.

turkey salsa tagliatelle

5½ POINTS VALUE

*This light, fresh tomato sauce is perfect for pasta but be warned, it is hot and fiery. To turn down the heat, either use less **jalapeño peppers** or use 1 large, de-seeded and diced **green pepper**. The **POINTS** values will remain the same.*

Serves 2
Takes *20 minutes*
11 *POINTS* *values per recipe*
472 calories *per serving*

150 g (5½ oz) dried tagliatelle
low fat cooking spray
250 g (9 oz) lean turkey breast steaks, cut into bite size strips
½ onion, chopped finely
1 garlic clove, crushed
25 g (1 oz) jalapeño peppers in brine, drained and chopped

5 ripe tomatoes, de-seeded and diced
½ x 25 g pack coriander, leaves chopped
salt and freshly ground black pepper

1 Bring a pan of water to the boil. Add the tagliatelle and cook for 10–12 minutes, or according to packet instructions, until al dente.

2 Meanwhile, heat a non stick frying pan until hot and spray with the cooking spray. Add the turkey strips and cook for 3 minutes until brown all over. Then add the onion and cook for 3 minutes. Stir in the garlic, jalapeño peppers and half the tomatoes. Gently cook for 3 minutes until warmed through and the turkey is cooked.

3 Drain the pasta, reserving a ladleful of cooking liquid in the pan. Return the pasta to the pan. Stir through the turkey mixture, remaining tomatoes and coriander. Check seasoning and serve immediately.

Ⓨ **Vegetarian option** You can replace the turkey with 175 g (6 oz) **Quorn Chicken Style Pieces** for 5 **POINTS** values per serving, or simply omit the turkey and use two more **tomatoes** for a simple sauce and 3½ **POINTS** values per serving.

all in one roast

Relax and enjoy this delicious roast for longer on those lazy Sunday afternoons - there's hardly any washing up to do, only one roasting tray.

Serves 4

Takes *10 minutes to prepare, 50 minutes to cook*

26½ POINTS *values per recipe*

310 calories *per serving*

1 tablespoon smoked paprika

4 x 240 g (8½ oz) chicken breast quarters, skin removed

350 g (12 oz) potatoes, peeled and cubed

2 preserved lemons from a jar, drained and sliced

2 garlic cloves, sliced

100 ml (3½ fl oz) hot chicken stock

50 g (1¾ oz) thin chorizo slices

2 tablespoons finely chopped fresh flat leaf parsley, to serve

1 Preheat the oven to Gas Mark 5/190°C/fan oven 170°C. Rub the paprika all over the chicken quarters and then put them into a deep roasting tin along with the potato cubes, preserved lemons and garlic. Pour over the stock and roast in the oven for 30 minutes.

2 Remove the roasting tin from the oven and scatter over the chorizo slices. Return to the oven and roast for a further 15–20 minutes until the potatoes are tender and the chicken is cooked and the juices run clear when a skewer is inserted. Sprinkle with the parsley and serve.

Variation If you can't find chicken quarters, you can use four (100 g/3½ oz) skinless drumsticks, and four (85 g/3 oz) thighs, for a **POINTS** value of 9 per serving.

spicy chicken laksa

Tom yum is a Thai spiced paste used for making traditional hot and sour soups and is available from most large supermarkets. If you can't find it, use 2 tablespoons of red Thai curry paste instead, for a **POINTS** value of 8 per serving.

Serves 4

Takes *30 minutes to prepare, 20 minutes to cook*

31 *POINTS* values per recipe

394 calories *per serving*

low fat cooking spray

4 x 150 g (5½ oz) skinless boneless chicken breasts, cut into bite size pieces

1 onion, sliced finely

1 red pepper, de-seeded and sliced finely

2 tablespoons tom yum paste

450 ml (16 fl oz) chicken stock

1 x 400 ml can reduced fat coconut milk

125 g (4½ oz) sugar snap peas

100 g (3½ oz) dried wholewheat noodles

1 x 220 g can bamboo shoots in water, drained

½ x 25 g pack fresh coriander, leaves only

lime wedges, to serve

1 Heat a lidded, deep, non stick saucepan and spray with the cooking spray. Add the chicken pieces and cook for 5 minutes, stirring until brown. You may need to do this in batches. Remove and set aside.

2 Add the onion and pepper to the saucepan and cook for 3–4 minutes until softened but not coloured. Stir in the tom yum paste and cook for 1 minute. Return the chicken pieces to the pan and pour in the stock and coconut milk. Bring to the boil, cover and simmer for 20 minutes.

3 Add the sugar snap peas, noodles and bamboo shoots. Cook, uncovered, for 2–3 minutes until tender, stirring occasionally to break up the noodles. Serve immediately in bowls and top with the coriander and lime wedges on the side.

Ⓨ **Vegetarian option** You can replace the chicken with a 350 g pack of **Quorn Chicken Style Pieces**, for a **POINTS** value of 6½ per serving.

creamy pesto pasta

7½ POINTS VALUE

*Why spend time and money at an Italian restaurant when you can cook something so simple, and just as tasty, at home? If you can't find fresh pesto, use 2 tablespoons of red pesto from a jar, for the same **POINTS** values per serving.*

Serves 4
Takes *20 minutes*
29 POINTS *values per recipe*
505 calories *per serving*

250 g (9 oz) dried trofie pasta, or other small pasta shapes
low fat cooking spray
500 g (1 lb 2 oz) turkey steaks, cut into short strips
2 garlic cloves, sliced
5 spring onions, trimmed and sliced finely
2 tablespoons fresh red pesto

150 g (5½ oz) half fat crème fraîche
75 g (2¾ oz) mild or hot pepperdew peppers in brine, drained and sliced finely
150 ml (5 fl oz) chicken stock
salt and freshly ground black pepper

1 Bring a large pan of water to the boil. Add the pasta, bring back to the boil and cook, according to the packet instructions, until al dente.
2 Meanwhile, heat a wide saucepan and spray with the cooking spray. Add the turkey and cook for 5 minutes, stirring until brown all over. You may have to do this in batches. Return all the turkey to the pan, add the garlic and spring onions and cook for a further 3 minutes.
3 Add the pesto, crème fraîche, peppers and stock. Bring just to the boil and check the seasoning. Drain the pasta and stir through the sauce. Serve immediately.

Ⓥ **Vegetarian option** You can use a 350 g pack of **Quorn Chicken Style Pieces**, instead of the turkey, for 7 **POINTS** values per serving.

paprika chicken

*Chicken thighs are full of
flavour and really moist, but
you can use 2 x 165 g
(5¾ oz)* **skinless boneless
chicken breasts** *instead,
for 3* **POINTS** *values per
serving.*

Serves 2

Takes *15 minutes to prepare,
10 minutes to cook*

15 *POINTS values per recipe*

256 calories *per serving*

2 teaspoons chicken gravy granules

1 tablespoon paprika

4 x 85 g (3 oz) skinless boneless chicken thighs

low fat cooking spray

2 tablespoons Worcestershire sauce

1 tablespoon tomato purée

1 Crush the gravy granules and paprika in a pestle and mortar to a fine powder.
  Put the chicken thighs on to a plate and sprinkle over the paprika powder, turning
  to coat thoroughly.

2 Heat a wide, lidded saucepan until hot and spray the chicken thighs with
  the cooking spray. Cook in the pan for 5 minutes until browned then add the
  Worcestershire sauce, tomato purée and 200 ml (7 fl oz) cold water. Bring to the
  boil. Cover and simmer for 10 minutes, turning halfway through until cooked.

3 Remove the chicken with a pair of tongs. Put on to a plate and cover with foil.
  Rapidly bubble the sauce for 1–2 minutes until thickened. Pour over the chicken
  and serve immediately.

Serving suggestion Try serving with 150 g (5½ oz) cooked new **potatoes**
per person and cooked **sugar snap peas**, for an extra 1½ **POINTS** values per
serving.

quick and easy

weeknight meals. They range from one pot wonders such as Texan Beef Chilli or Satay Pork to do-ahead dinners like Sesame Porkballs and Really Easy Mousakka. All the recipes in this chapter are satisfying and leave you feeling fuller for longer. Why not try the Mushroom Spiced Steak or Balsamic Lamb Chops? Or if you're looking for the traditional meat and veg kind of dinner, the Olive Crusted Pork is a great choice. When the end of the week finally arrives, treat yourself and enjoy the Roasted Pork Loin with an Apple Crust or the fantastic Greek Roast Lamb.

Balsamic Lamb Chops, page 71

beef and shiitake mushroom stir fry

The secret to a good stir fry is to have all the ingredients prepared before you get cooking. That way everything cooks perfectly and retains some crunch.

Serves 2
Takes *20 minutes*
6 POINTS *values per recipe*
248 calories *per serving*

100 g (3½ oz) tenderstem broccoli
225 g (8 oz) fillet steak**, cut into thin strips**
low fat cooking spray
2 garlic cloves**, sliced**
25 g (1 oz) fresh ginger, peeled and cut into matchsticks
100 g (3½ oz) shiitake mushrooms**, trimmed and sliced**
½ red pepper**, de-seeded and diced finely**
50 ml (2 fl oz) teriyaki sauce
juice of a lime

1 Cut the florets from the broccoli stalks and set aside. Then cut the broccoli stalks in half lengthways and then in half again to make short stems. Set aside.

2 Heat a wok or non stick frying pan until really hot. Spray the steak with the cooking spray and stir fry for 5 minutes, stirring constantly, until brown. Remove and set aside. Spray the pan again and add the garlic and ginger and stir fry for 1 minute.

3 Add the mushrooms, pepper, broccoli florets and stalks. Stir fry for 3–4 minutes, stirring occasionally until just tender. Return the beef and add the teriyaki sauce. Remove from the heat, as it will bubble very quickly due to the heat of the pan. Squeeze over the lime, stir once more and serve immediately.

Serving suggestion Enjoy with 40 g (1½ oz) dried rice noodles per person, cooked according to the packet instructions, for an extra 2 **POINTS** values per serving.

Ⓨ **Vegetarian option** You can replace the beef with 300 g (10½ oz) mixed mushrooms such as oyster, chestnut and portabello. This will be 0 **POINTS** values per serving.

mushroom spiced steak

3½ POINTS VALUE

Dried mushrooms really give a flavoursome crust to the steak.

Serves 4

Takes *20 minutes*

14½ POINTS *values per recipe*

180 calories *per serving*

goes well with...

The Breaded Garlic Mushrooms on page 175, for an extra 2 POINTS values per serving.

2 x 300 g (10½ oz) **sirloin steaks, visible fat removed and each cut in half**

½ x 25 g pack dried **porcini mushrooms**

1 teaspoon garlic granules

1 tablespoon fresh thyme leaves

low fat cooking spray

freshly ground black pepper

1 Put the steaks on a board and cover with clingfilm. Using a meat hammer or a rolling pin, bash the steak until 1 cm (½ inch) thick. Put the dried mushrooms, garlic, thyme and freshly ground black pepper into a food processor, and whizz until a coarse powder. Transfer to a plate.

2 Press one side of each steak into the mushroom powder until coated. Heat a griddle pan or non stick frying pan until hot. Spray the steaks with the cooking spray and cook in the pan, mushroom side down for 2–3 minutes.

3 Turn over and cook for a further 3–4 minutes until charred and cooked to your liking. Transfer to a plate, cover with foil and leave to rest for 5 minutes. Serve immediately after the resting time, and drizzle over any juices from the plate.

Serving suggestion Serve with 70 g (2½ oz) cooked broad beans, grilled tomato halves and 150 g (5½ oz) baked potato wedges per person, for an extra 2½ **POINTS** values per serving.

3½ POINTS VALUE

sesame porkballs

This is the perfect food for sharing with friends. Put the porkballs and hoisin sauce in the middle of the table and let everyone help themselves.

❋ *raw pork balls only*

Serves 4

Takes *15 minutes to prepare, 15 minutes to cook*

16 POINTS *values per recipe (using less than 7% fat pork mince)*

237 calories *per serving*

5 spring onions

a generous pinch of chilli flakes

½ x 25 g pack fresh coriander

500 g (1lb 2 oz) less than 7% fat lean pork mince

2 teaspoons soy sauce

2 teaspoons Thai fish sauce

30 g (1¼ oz) sesame seeds

4 tablespoons hoisin sauce, to serve

1 Preheat the oven to Gas Mark 6/200°C/fan oven 180°C. Put the spring onions, chilli flakes and coriander into a food processor, and whizz until finely minced. Add the pork mince, soy sauce and fish sauce. Blend again briefly until mixed. Using wet hands, roll the pork mixture into 20 small balls.

2 Sprinkle the sesame seeds on to a plate and then roll the pork balls in the seeds, one at a time to coat lightly. Place on a non stick baking tray and bake in the oven for 15 minutes until cooked. Serve five pork balls each, with the hoisin sauce to dip into.

Serving suggestion Serve with mixed stir fry vegetables, such as pak choi, peppers and shiitake mushrooms as well as 40 g (1½ oz) dried rice noodles per person, cooked according to the packet instructions, for an extra 2 **POINTS** values per serving.

Variation This also works really well with the same quantity of golden linseeds, in place of the sesame seeds, for the same **POINTS** values.

Tip If using regular pork mince, the **POINTS** values will be 5½ per serving.

balsamic lamb chops

When cooked, the vinegar caramelizes, making the lamb rich, sweet and tangy. The longer you marinate the lamb, the more intense the flavour.

Serves 4

Takes *30 minutes*

18½ POINTS *values per recipe*

112 calories *per serving*

goes well with...
The Rhubarb and Custard Pots on page 187, for an extra 1½ POINTS values per serving.

8 x 100 g (3½ oz) lamb chops, visible fat removed

4 tablespoons balsamic vinegar

1 teaspoon mint sauce

1 teaspoon dried chilli flakes

350 g (12 oz) asparagus spears, trimmed

low fat cooking spray

300 g (10½ oz) cherry tomatoes on the vine

salt and freshly ground black pepper

1 Preheat the grill to medium hot. Put the lamb chops in a shallow dish and sprinkle over the balsamic vinegar, mint sauce, chill flakes and seasoning.

2 Put the chops on a grill pan lined with foil and cook under the grill for 10–15 minutes, turning and basting with any juices until cooked to your liking. Transfer to a warm plate, cover with foil and set aside.

3 Put the asparagus on to the grill pan and spray with the cooking spray. Grill for 5 minutes then add the cherry tomatoes and cook for a further 2–3 minutes until the asparagus begins to char and is tender and the tomatoes just burst. Serve the lamb immediately with the asparagus and tomatoes, with the pan juices drizzled over.

Serving suggestion Serve with 150 g (5½ oz) boiled potatoes per person, for an additional 1½ **POINTS** values per serving.

creamy peppercorn beef

Serve with 150 g (5½ oz) cooked brown rice per person and green beans, for an extra 3 POINTS values per serving.

Serves 2
Takes *15 minutes*
9 POINTS *values per recipe*
282 calories *per serving*

goes well with...

The Slow Roasted Plums on page 186, for an extra ½ POINTS value per serving.

275 g (9½ oz) **sirloin steak, cut into 1 cm (¼ inch) thick slices**
1 teaspoon **paprika**
low fat cooking spray
75 ml (3 fl oz) **Worcestershire sauce**
1 teaspoon **green peppercorns in brine, drained and crushed lightly**
100 g (3½ oz) **low fat soft cheese with garlic and herbs**
150 ml (5 fl oz) **beef stock**
2 tablespoons **freshly chopped curly parsley, to garnish**

1 Put the steak slices in a bowl and sprinkle with the paprika, turning until coated. Heat a non stick frying pan and spray with the cooking spray. Cook the steak slices for 3 minutes until brown, stirring halfway. Remove to a plate and cover with foil to keep warm.

2 Pour the Worcestershire sauce into the pan and bubble for 2 minutes. Add the peppercorns and whisk in the soft cheese. Gradually pour in the stock and simmer for 2–3 minutes. Return the beef and any juices to the pan. Simmer for 1–2 minutes until thickened. Sprinkle with parsley and serve immediately.

tandoori lamb

Serve with a Weight Watchers Mini Plain Naan (55 g) per person and a mixed leaf salad, for an extra 2 POINTS values per serving.

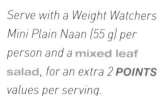 *lamb only*
Serves 2
Takes *50 minutes*
9 POINTS *values per recipe*
242 calories *per serving*

2 teaspoons **tandoori curry paste**
2 tablespoons **freshly chopped coriander**
1 tablespoon **smooth mango chutney**
2 x 100 g (3½ oz) **lean lamb leg steaks**
200 g (7 oz) **new potatoes, such as Charlotte or Jersey Royal, scrubbed and halved**
75 g (2¾ oz) **low fat natural yogurt**
1 tablespoon **mint sauce**
75 g (2¾ oz) **cucumber, de-seeded and diced**
½ **small red onion, sliced finely**

1 To make a marinade, mix together the tandoori paste, coriander and mango chutney in a non metallic bowl. Add the lamb steaks and coat in the marinade. Set aside for 30 minutes.

2 Meanwhile, put the potatoes in a lidded saucepan and cover with cold water. Bring to the boil and simmer, covered, for 20 minutes until tender. Drain and leave to cool.

3 Preheat the grill to medium. Put the lamb on a foil lined grill pan and grill for 8–12 minutes, turning halfway until charred and cooked to your liking. Remove from the grill, cover loosely with foil and set aside.

4 Mix together the yogurt, mint sauce, cucumber and onion with the potatoes. Serve with the tandoori lamb.

sensational flavour

olive crusted pork

This topping is a fantastic way to liven up a pork steak and helps to keep it really moist.

Serves 2

Takes *10 minutes to prepare, 20 minutes to cook*

9 *POINTS* values per recipe

432 calories *per serving*

goes well with...

The Vanilla and Passion Fruit Cups on page 188, for an additional 1½ POINTS values per serving.

2 x 150 g (5½ oz) lean pork loin steaks, **visible fat removed**
low fat cooking spray
2 x 15 g (½ oz) wholewheat crispbreads
60 g (2 oz) pitted green olives **in brine, drained and chopped**
1 garlic clove, **crushed**
1 teaspoon Dijon mustard
1 tablespoon freshly chopped flat leaf parsley

1 Preheat the oven to Gas Mark 6/200°C /fan oven 180°C . Heat a non stick frying pan and spray the pork steaks with the cooking spray. Cook for 3–4 minutes, turning halfway until brown all over. Remove and place on a baking tray.

2 In a food processor, whizz the crispbreads, olives, garlic, half the mustard and all of the parsley until it forms a coarse mixture (it will come together).

3 Brush the remaining mustard over one side of each pork steak and press half the olive mixture on top of each. Bake in the oven for 15–20 minutes until golden.

Serving suggestion Serve with a 2 x 60 g (2 oz) scoop of mashed potato per person and chargrilled courgettes and peppers, for an extra 1½ **POINTS** values per serving.

nutty lamb kebabs

The longer you leave the lamb to marinate, the more intense the flavour. These work really well when cooked on the BBQ as a great summertime feast.

❊ *marinated lamb only*

Serves 4

Takes *20 minutes*

17 POINTS *values per recipe*

224 calories *per serving*

goes well with...

The Carrot and Courgette Spiced Salad on page 170, for an extra 1 POINTS value per serving.

500 g (1 lb 2 oz) lean boneless leg of lamb, **trimmed of visible fat and cut into cubes**

2 tablespoons low fat natural yogurt

2 tablespoons finely chopped fresh mint

1 garlic clove, **crushed**

zest and juice of a lemon

50 g (1¾ oz) pistachio nuts

50 g (1¾ oz) redcurrant jelly, melted

1 Preheat the grill to hot. Put the lamb cubes in a bowl and mix with the yogurt, mint, garlic, lemon zest and juice. Set aside. Whizz the pistachios in a food processor, or blender, until chopped finely. Put on to a plate and set aside.

2 Thread the lamb on to four metal skewers and put on to a foil lined grill pan. Cook under the grill for 8–10 minutes, turning and basting with the redcurrant jelly until starting to char. When the lamb is cooked, quickly roll the skewers in the nuts and serve immediately.

Serving suggestion Delicious with a 225 g (8 oz) jacket potato per person, for an extra 2½ **POINTS** values per serving.

gammon rosti bake

4½ POINTS VALUE

This twist on the classic pineapple and gammon will soon become a family favourite.

Serves 4

Takes *15 minutes to prepare + cooling, 20 minutes to cook*

18½ POINTS *values per recipe*

217 calories *per serving*

150 g (5½ oz) waxy potatoes such as Désirée, peeled and cut into even chunks

75 g (2¾ oz) celeriac, peeled and cut into even chunks

½ small onion, peeled and grated

1 tablespoon snipped fresh chives

1 tablespoon wholegrain mustard

1 x 450 g pack two smoked gammon steaks, fat trimmed and each cut in half

1 x 227 g can pineapple rings in natural juice, drained

low fat cooking spray

freshly ground black pepper

1 Preheat the oven to Gas Mark 6/200°C/fan oven 180°C. Put the potato and celeriac in a saucepan and cover with water. Bring to the boil and simmer for 5 minutes. Drain and leave to cool for 5–10 minutes.

2 When cool enough to handle, grate the potato and celeriac into a large bowl and season with freshly ground black pepper. Add the grated onion to the potato mixture. Stir in the chives and mustard.

3 Put the gammon steaks on to a baking tray and top each steak with a pineapple ring. Press the grated potato mixture on top of the pineapple. Spray with the cooking spray and bake in the oven for 20 minutes until golden and cooked. Serve immediately.

Serving suggestion Serve with cooked French beans and 70 g (2½ oz) cooked peas per person, for an extra 1 **POINTS** value per serving.

Greek roast lamb

Serves 4

Takes *25 minutes to prepare,
1 hour 20–30 minutes to cook
+ 10 minutes resting*

20½ POINTS *values per
recipe*

270 calories *per serving*

goes well with...
**The Red Wine Gravy on
page 172, for an extra
1½ POINTS values per
serving.**

600 g (1 lb 5 oz) lean boneless leg of lamb

zest and juice of a lemon

1 x 410 g can chick peas **in water, drained and rinsed**

30 g (1¼ oz) kalamata olive tapenade

1 garlic clove, **crushed**

1 tablespoon freshly chopped oregano

freshly ground black pepper

1 Preheat the oven to Gas Mark 5/190°C/fan oven 170°C. Unroll the lamb and place on to a board, with the thin layer of fat on the bottom. Carefully cut two horizontal cuts into the lamb, either side of the centre, eventually enabling you to roll the meat out flat and open up like a book. Put the lamb in a shallow dish, cut side up and sprinkle with the lemon zest, juice and lots of freshly ground black pepper. Set aside.

2 Meanwhile, blend half the chick peas in a food processor, or using a hand blender, until finely minced. Transfer to a bowl and mix with the tapenade, garlic, oregano, freshly ground black pepper and remaining chick peas. Press the stuffing along the length of the lamb, then re-roll and tie with kitchen string in about five places. If any stuffing comes out, squidge it back in.

3 Place in a roasting tin and roast for 1 hour 20 minutes until cooked, it will be a little pink in the middle. For well done, cook for a further 10 minutes. Cover loosely with foil and rest for 10 minutes. Carve in thick slices and serve.

Serving suggestion Finish off the meal with zero **POINTS** value green vegetables and 100 g (3½ oz) potatoes (roasted in low fat cooking spray) per person, for an extra 1 **POINTS** value per serving.

really easy moussaka

Forget salting aubergine slices for hours – this quick version of the Greek classic saves you loads of time in the kitchen, meaning you can put your feet up while it cooks.

Serves 6

Takes *20 minutes to prepare, 55 minutes to cook*

33½ POINTS *values per recipe*

273 calories *per serving*

500 g (1 lb 2 oz) lean lamb mince

1 garlic clove, **crushed**

1 aubergine, **cut into 1 cm (¼ inch) cubes**

2 teaspoons dried oregano

1 teaspoon mint sauce

200 g (7 oz) passata with onion and garlic

300 g (10½ oz) potatoes, **peeled and sliced really thinly**

350 g (12 oz) Quark

1 egg yolk

a little freshly grated nutmeg

salt and freshly ground pepper

1 Preheat the oven to Gas Mark 4/180°C/fan oven 160°C. Heat a non stick, deep and wide frying pan. Cook the lamb for 5 minutes, breaking up with a wooden spoon until brown. Add the garlic, aubergine, oregano and mint sauce. Cook for 5 minutes. Stir in the passata and spoon into a 1.75 litre (3 pint) ovenproof dish.

2 Arrange the potatoes in a single layer over the top. In a bowl, mix together the Quark and egg yolk and season. Spread over the top of the potatoes and sprinkle with a little nutmeg. Bake in the oven for 50–55 minutes until golden and the potatoes are cooked. Serve immediately.

Serving suggestion Serve with a generous zero **POINTS** value salad, mixed with fat free salad dressing, for no additional **POINTS** values.

crunchy beef salad

6½ POINTS VALUE

This delicious Thai inspired beef noodle dish also works well with leftover roast beef. Simply use 2 x 35 g medium slices roast beef per serving instead of the steak, for the same POINTS values per serving.

Serves 2

Takes *20 minutes*

13 POINTS *values per recipe*

437 calories *per serving*

100 g (3½ oz) cucumber, de-seeded and grated coarsely

100 g (3½ oz) beansprouts

½ red pepper, de-seeded and sliced finely

2 tablespoons freshly chopped coriander

1–2 teaspoons wasabi paste

1 tablespoon sweet chilli sauce

juice of a lime

½ teaspoon fish sauce

2 teaspoons light soy sauce

2 x 125 g (4½ oz) fillet steak

low fat cooking spray

75 g (2¾ oz) dried rice noodles, broken in half

15 g (½ oz) dry roasted peanuts, chopped

1 In a large bowl, mix together the cucumber, beansprouts, pepper and coriander. Set aside. In a small jug, mix together the wasabi, chilli sauce, lime juice, fish sauce and soy sauce.

2 Heat a griddle pan or non stick frying pan until hot and spray the steaks with cooking spray. Cook for 5–6 minutes, turning halfway until cooked to your liking. Remove to a plate, cover loosely with foil and set aside for 5 minutes.

3 Meanwhile, soak the rice noodles in half a kettle of boiling water and set aside for 5 minutes. Drain and gently toss the noodles and dressing through the beansprout salad. Divide between two plates, slice the steak on the diagonal and place on top of the salads. Sprinkle over the peanuts and serve.

roasted pork loin with an apple crust

Serves 4

Takes *20 minutes to prepare, 1 hour 20 minutes to cook*

25½ POINTS *values per recipe*

318 calories *per serving*

low fat cooking spray

1 small onion, diced finely

1 red eating apple, cored and grated

4 fresh sage leaves, chopped finely

30 g (1¼ oz) fresh breadcrumbs

600 g (1 lb 5 oz) boneless pork loin joint, visible fat removed

1 egg yolk

1 teaspoon Dijon mustard

1 x 500 ml bottle dry cider

1 tablespoon plain flour

1 Preheat the oven to Gas Mark 5/190°C/fan oven 170°C. Heat a non stick frying pan and spray with the cooking spray. Cook the onion, apple and sage for 3–4 minutes until softened but not coloured. Empty into a bowl and mix with the breadcrumbs. Set aside.

2 Heat the frying pan again and spray the pork with the cooking spray. Cook the pork for 5 minutes, turning until brown all over. Remove and set aside.

3 Mix the egg yolk into the apple and breadcrumbs until combined. Brush the mustard over the top of the pork and then carefully press on the apple and breadcrumb mixture. Put the joint in a roasting tin and pour the cider around. Cover with foil and roast in the oven for 1 hour 20 minutes or until the juices run clear, removing the foil after 1 hour.

4 Transfer the pork to a board and cover loosely with foil to keep warm. Carefully pour the pork juices from the roasting tin into a jug. Sprinkle the flour into the roasting tin and put on the hob. Gradually pour the juices back into the roasting tin, stirring constantly, scraping the residue from the pan until combined. Bring to the boil and simmer for 1–2 minutes until thickened. Carve the pork into slices and serve with the cider gravy.

Serving suggestion Serve with 100 g (3½ oz) cooked potato per person, mashed with 75 g (2¾ oz) cooked carrot and lots of tenderstem broccoli, for an extra 1 **POINTS** value per serving.

Texan beef chilli

Everyone loves a bowl of spicy chilli. Enjoy with a crisp green zero POINTS value salad.

Serves 4
Takes *10 minutes to prepare, 30 minutes to cook*
26½ POINTS *values per recipe*
287 calories *per serving*

low fat cooking spray
500 g (1 lb 2 oz) lean beef mince
2 garlic cloves, crushed
1 tablespoon mild or hot chilli powder
2 tablespoons tomato purée
125 ml (4 fl oz) red wine
150 ml (5 fl oz) beef stock
1 x 410 g can kidney beans in water, drained and rinsed
6 tablespoons smoky BBQ sauce

1 Heat a wide, non stick saucepan and spray with the cooking spray. Add the beef mince and cook for 5 minutes, breaking up the meat with two wooden spoons. Add the garlic and chilli powder and cook for 2 minutes.

2 Stir in the tomato purée, red wine, beef stock, kidney beans and BBQ sauce. Simmer for 30 minutes until thickened. Serve immediately.

Serving suggestion Put the chilli in two 12 g tacos, and then top with salad leaves and shredded onion, for an extra 2 **POINTS** values per serving.

ⓥ **Vegetarian option** You can use a 350 g pack of vegetarian mince instead of the beef mince, for 4 **POINTS** values per serving.

impress your friends

satay pork

7½ POINTS VALUE

This is delicious with rice noodles.

Serves 2
Takes 20 minutes
15 POINTS values per recipe
383 calories per serving

low fat cooking spray
250 g (9 oz) lean pork tenderloin, sliced thickly
1 garlic clove, crushed
1–2 teaspoons dried chilli flakes
1 large carrot, peeled and cut into matchsticks
75 g (2¾ oz) mange tout, halved on the diagonal

½ sweet red pepper, de-seeded and sliced in rings
juice of a lime, plus wedges to serve
30 g (1¼ oz) smooth reduced fat peanut butter
½ x 400 ml can reduced fat coconut milk
200 ml (7 fl oz) chicken stock

1 Heat a wide, deep non stick frying pan until hot and spray with the cooking spray. Cook the pork for 5 minutes, turning until brown. Add the garlic, chilli flakes, carrot, mange tout and pepper and fry for a further 5 minutes until softened.
2 Mix together the lime juice, peanut butter, coconut milk and stock in a jug.
3 Transfer the pork and vegetables to a warm plate and cover with foil. Pour the coconut milk mixture into the pan. Gently simmer for 1–2 minutes until thickened.
4 Return the pork and vegetables to the pan, stirring to coat and heat through. Serve immediately with lime wedges on the side.

Serving suggestion Serve 40 g (1½ oz) dried rice noodles per person, cooked according to the packet instructions, for an extra 2 **POINTS** values per serving.

Preparing delicious and nutritious weeknight meals for the whole family is simple with these tried and tested recipes - they're easy to make, full of foods to fill you up and everyone will love them. With favourites such as Special Pork Chow Mein, Chicken Cordon Bleu and Oven Baked Fish and Chips, you'll never be stuck again for an answer to 'What's for dinner?'. For a delicious vegetarian meal, the Crispy Cauliflower Gratin or Veggie Sausage Ragu will hit the spot. If you're in the mood for food from around the globe, Caribbean Meatballs will add a bit of spice, Italian Haddock Bake takes you to the Med and Eastern Prawn Salad is a delicious Oriental delight. Whatever you fancy, there's one for every day of the week, the only problem will be which one to cook first.

Caribbean Meatballs, *page 94*

Eastern prawn salad

This will last for 2 days in the fridge.

Serves 4
Takes *10 minutes to prepare,*
20 minutes to cook
9 POINTS *values per recipe*
188 calories *per serving*

125 g (4½ oz) **dried** brown basmati rice
a kettle full of boiling water
300 g (10½ oz) **cooked and peeled** tiger prawns
100 g (3½ oz) cherry tomatoes, **halved**
1 x 220 g **can whole** water chestnuts in water, **drained and**
    quartered
2 tablespoons freshly chopped coriander
zest and juice of 2 limes
2 teaspoons Chinese 5 spice powder
a generous pinch of dried chilli flakes
100 g (3½ oz) fine green beans, **trimmed and cut in half**

1 Put the rice into a large, lidded saucepan and cover with boiling water from the
  kettle. Bring back to the boil, cover and simmer for 20 minutes.
2 Meanwhile, in a large bowl stir together the prawns, tomatoes, chestnuts,
  coriander, lime zest and juice, Chinese 5 spice powder and chilli flakes. Set aside.
3 Add the green beans to the rice and cook for the final minute. Drain and rinse in
  cold water. Drain again, ensuring it is drained thoroughly.
4 Stir the cooked rice and beans into the prawns and serve immediately.

Serving suggestion Serve with ¼ x 90 g bag of prawn crackers each, for an
extra 2½ **POINTS** values per serving.

Italian haddock bake

Serves 4

Takes *15 minutes to prepare, 45 minutes to cook*

11½ POINTS *values per recipe*

399 calories *per serving*

goes well with...

The Polenta and Olive Chips on page 182, for an additional 3 POINTS values per serving.

2 mixed peppers, de-seeded and sliced

1 red onion, chopped roughly

2 garlic cloves, sliced

1 fennel bulb, diced roughly

low fat cooking spray

100 g (3½ oz) low fat soft cheese

1 tablespoon chopped fresh dill

15 g (½ oz) capers in brine, drained and chopped finely

30 g (1¼ oz) gherkins, diced finely

4 x 150 g (5½ oz) skinless haddock loin fillets

1 tablespoon Italian mixed herbs

150 g (5½ oz) cherry tomatoes, halved

1 x 185 g can pitted black olives in brine, drained

freshly ground black pepper

1 Preheat the oven to Gas Mark 6/200°C/fan oven 180°C. Put the peppers, onion, garlic and fennel in a shallow roasting pan and spray with the cooking spray. Roast in the oven for 30 minutes, stirring the vegetables halfway through.

2 Meanwhile, in a small bowl, mix together the soft cheese, dill, capers, gherkins and freshly ground black pepper. Lay the haddock fillets on a board and generously spread one side of each fillet with the soft cheese mixture. Set aside.

3 Remove the vegetables from the oven and stir in the dried herbs. Scatter over the tomatoes and olives and lay the haddock fillets on top of the vegetables, with a little gap between each fillet. Bake in the oven for a further 10–15 minutes until cooked and golden. Serve immediately.

chicken Cordon Bleu

In the traditional version of this dish, the ham would be in the middle with the cheese, but putting it on the outside helps to keep the chicken moist and stops the filling from oozing out.

4 x 165 g (5¾ oz) skinless boneless chicken breasts

100 g (3½ oz) low fat soft cheese with garlic and herbs

25 g (1 oz) black olives **in brine, drained and chopped finely**

2 sprigs of fresh rosemary**, each cut in half**

8 x 10 g (¼ oz) smoked wafer thin ham

low fat cooking spray

salt and freshly ground black pepper

Serves 4

Takes *10 minutes to prepare, 20 minutes to cook*

15 POINTS *values per recipe*

232 calories *per serving*

goes well with...

The Citrus Slaw on page 169, for an extra ½ POINTS value per serving.

1 Preheat the oven to Gas Mark 6/200°C/fan oven 180°C. Cut a pocket into the thickest part of each chicken breast. Mix together the soft cheese, olives and seasoning. Divide to fill each chicken pocket.

2 Put a sprig of rosemary on top of each chicken breast and then seal the pocket and hold the sprig of rosemary in place with two slices of ham like a plaster. Spray with the cooking spray, transfer to a non stick baking tray and bake in the oven for 15–20 minutes until cooked. Serve immediately.

Serving suggestion Serve with 100 g (3½ oz) new potatoes per person and a mixed green zero **POINTS** value salad, for an extra 1 **POINTS** value per serving.

special pork chow mein

Look for the fresh noodles in the vegetable aisle at the supermarket, beside the packs of stir fry veggies.

Serves 4

Takes *40 minutes*

18 POINTS *values per recipe*

230 calories *per serving*

goes well with...

The Quick Banana Ice Cream on page 200, for an extra 3½ *POINTS* values per serving.

400 g (14 oz) lean pork tenderloin

1 tablespoon tandoori spice mix

low fat cooking spray

4 tablespoons dark soy sauce

2 tablespoons rice wine vinegar

2 teaspoons tomato purée

1 garlic clove, crushed

1 red chilli, sliced finely

1 x 120 g pack shiitake mushrooms, wiped and sliced

1 carrot, peeled and cut into thin matchsticks

2 small pak choi, leaves separated from the stalks and stalks sliced finely, then both reserved

1 x 400 g pack fresh egg noodles

60 g (2 oz) beansprouts

1 Preheat the oven to Gas Mark 6/200°C/fan oven 180°C and put a baking tray in to heat. Coat the pork in the tandoori spice mix and spray with the cooking spray. Heat a non stick frying pan until hot and cook the pork for 5 minutes, turning so that each side is brown. Remove the baking tray from the oven, transfer the pork to the tray and cook in the oven for 10–15 minutes until cooked.

2 After 10 minutes, mix together the soy sauce, vinegar and tomato purée in a small jug. Set aside. Heat a wok or non stick frying pan until hot and spray with the cooking spray. Stir fry the garlic and chilli for 1 minute, then add the mushrooms, carrots and pak choi stalks and cook for 5 minutes. Take off the heat.

3 Remove the pork from the oven and cover loosely with foil to keep warm. Set aside. Put the pan or wok back on the heat and add the noodles, beansprouts and pak choi leaves. Stir fry for 3 minutes. Pour in the soy sauce mixture and cook gently for 1 minute, stirring until coated and combined. Divide the noodles between warm bowls, thinly slice the pork and place on top of the noodles. Serve immediately.

crispy cauliflower gratin

What could be better than a cross between macaroni cheese and cauliflower cheese? This can be made up to a day ahead to the end of step 2 and then chilled until needed. Bring back to room temperature before cooking.

Ⓥ Serves 4

Takes *10 minutes to prepare, 40 minutes to cook*
19 POINTS *values per recipe*
295 calories *per serving*

450 ml (16 fl oz) skimmed milk
2 garlic cloves, **sliced**
1 tablespoon fresh thyme **leaves**
30 g (1¼ oz) cornflour
100 g (3½ oz) Gruyère cheese, grated
1 small cauliflower **(about 225 g/8 oz), cored and cut into small florets**
125 g (4½ oz) fresh penne pasta
salt and freshly ground black pepper

1 Preheat the oven to Gas Mark 5/190°C/fan oven 170°C. Bring a large pan of water to the boil. Meanwhile, put the milk, garlic and thyme into a pan and bring just to the boil. Mix a little of the hot milk with the cornflour to make a smooth paste and then stir back into the hot milk liquid. Gently heat for 1 minute, stirring until thick. Stir in half the Gruyère, season and set aside.

2 Plunge the cauliflower and pasta into the boiling water and simmer for 3 minutes. Drain and return to the pan. Pour the cheese sauce into the cauliflower pan and stir to coat. Transfer to a 1½ litre (2¾ pint) ovenproof dish and level the top.

3 Scatter over the remaining Gruyère cheese and bake in the oven for 35–40 minutes until golden and bubbling. Serve immediately.

Serving suggestion Serve with a large mixed salad and a 50 g (1¾ oz) bread roll per person, for an extra 2 *POINTS* values per serving.

rich and creamy

mushroom carbonara

Bucatini is a thick spaghetti which is really good for creamy sauces, but you could use tagliatelle or spaghetti instead, for the same *POINTS* values.

Ⓥ Serves 4

Takes *25 minutes*
20 POINTS *values per recipe*
384 calories *per serving*

300 g (10½ oz) dried bucatini
1 x 25 g pack dried porcini mushrooms
150 ml (5 fl oz) boiling water
low fat cooking spray
1 red onion, diced finely
1 garlic clove, crushed

300 g (10½ oz) baby portabello mushrooms, wiped, trimmed and sliced
1 x 250 g pot Quark
2 egg yolks
1 tablespoon snipped fresh chives
salt and freshly ground black pepper

1 Bring a pan of water to the boil, add the bucatini and cook for 7–8 minutes, or according to packet instructions, until al dente. Meanwhile, put the dried mushrooms into a small bowl and cover with the boiling water. Set aside.

2 Heat a non stick frying pan and spray with the cooking spray. Gently cook the onion for 3–4 minutes until softened. Add the garlic and sliced portabello mushrooms and cook for a further 5 minutes. Remove from the heat.

3 Add the Quark, egg yolks and soaked mushrooms and their soaking liquid to the pan. Stir until smooth. Return to the heat. Gently heat for 1 minute until slightly thickened. Drain the pasta, return to the pan and stir in the cooked mushroom mixture and chives. Check the seasoning. Serve immediately in shallow bowls.

quick grilled lamb

The longer you leave the mint paste on the chops the more intense the flavour.

Serves 2
Takes *15 minutes*
10 POINTS *values per recipe*
324 calories *per serving*

2 **garlic cloves**, chopped roughly
zest of a lemon
1 x 25 g pack fresh **mint**, leaves only
4 x 100 g (3½ oz) **lamb chops**, trimmed of all fat
low fat cooking spray
200 ml (7 fl oz) boiling water
1 teaspoon marmite
2½ teaspoons gravy granules
salt and freshly ground black pepper

1 Preheat the grill to hot. In a mortar and pestle, bash the garlic, lemon zest, mint and seasoning to a coarse paste. Spread a little over each lamb chop.
2 Put the lamb on a foil lined grill pan and spray with the cooking spray. Grill for 5–8 minutes until cooked to your liking, turning halfway through. Remove from the grill, cover loosely with foil and set aside.
3 Put the boiling water in a jug and mix in the marmite and gravy granules, stirring until thickened. Add any juices from the lamb and serve drizzled over the chops.

Serving suggestion Serve with 100 g (3½ oz) halved new potatoes, roasted with low fat cooking spray, 70 g (2½ oz) cooked, crushed peas per person and cooked carrots, for an extra 2 **POINTS** values per serving.

Tip If you don't have a mortar and pestle, blend the garlic, lemon zest and mint in a small food processor, or use a hand blender.

Caribbean meatballs

Serve with 150 g (5½ oz) cooked brown rice per person, for an extra 3 POINTS values per serving.

Serves 4
Takes *15 minutes to prepare, 30 minutes to cook*
20½ POINTS *values per recipe*
198 calories *per serving*

500 g (1 lb 2 oz) lean beef mince
1 x 25 g pack fresh **coriander**, chopped finely
zest and juice of a lime
1½ **tablespoons Jamaican jerk spices**
low fat cooking spray
1 **red pepper**, de-seeded and sliced finely
½ **onion**, sliced
1 x 400 g can **chopped tomatoes**
150 ml (5 fl oz) beef stock

1 In a large bowl, mix together the beef mince, coriander, lime zest and juice and 1 tablespoon of jerk spices with your hands. Divide and roll into 20 small balls.
2 Heat a wide, non stick lidded pan and spray with the cooking spray. Gently fry the meatballs for 5 minutes, turning until brown all over. You may need to do this in batches. Remove and set aside.
3 Add the pepper and onion to the pan. Cook for 3–4 minutes until starting to soften. Stir in the chopped tomatoes, beef stock and remaining jerk spices. Return the meatballs. Bring to the boil, cover and simmer for 20 minutes until the meatballs are cooked. Remove the lid and simmer for a further 5–10 minutes until the sauce is thickened. Serve immediately.

creamy lamb korma

Serves 4
Takes *1 hour*
24½ POINTS *values per recipe*
306 calories *per serving*

50 g (1¾ oz) unsalted cashew nuts
400 g (14 oz) lean boneless lamb leg steak**, visible fat removed, and cubed**
1 teaspoon ground turmeric
low fat cooking spray

2 tablespoons korma curry paste
200 ml (7 fl oz) lamb stock
1 x 410 g can chick peas **in water, drained and rinsed**
100 g (3½ oz) low fat soft cheese
2 tablespoons freshly chopped coriander**, to garnish**

1 Heat a deep, lidded non stick saucepan and dry fry the cashew nuts for 1–2 minutes until golden. Remove to a board and chop roughly. In a bowl, mix the lamb cubes with the turmeric.

2 Heat the pan again and spray with the cooking spray. Cook the lamb for 5 minutes, until brown all over. You may need to do this in batches. Return all the lamb to the pan. Add the curry paste and half the cashews and cook for 2 minutes.

3 Stir in the stock, bring to the boil and simmer for 40 minutes, until the lamb is really tender. Stir in the chick peas and soft cheese and gently heat until thickened. Serve immediately, sprinkled with the coriander and remaining cashew nuts.

Serving suggestion Serve with lots of spinach cooked with garlic and dried chilli flakes and one Weight Watchers plain poppadom per person, for an extra **1 POINTS** value per serving.

oven baked fish and chips

Enjoy delicious, home made, golden and crispy beer batter, without a deep fat fryer in sight.

Serves 4

Takes *10 minutes to prepare, 45 minutes to cook*

23 POINTS *values per recipe*

371 calories *per serving*

goes well with...

The Frozen Raspberry Tiramisu on page 194, for an extra 2½ POINTS values per serving.

500 g (1 lb 2 oz) potatoes, peeled and cut into 1 cm (¼ inch) thick chips

low fat cooking spray

4 x 150 g (5½ oz) skinless cod loin fillets

50 g (1¾ oz) low fat polyunsaturated margarine

100 g (3½ oz) plain flour

½ teaspoon bicarbonate of soda

1 egg, beaten

50 ml (2 fl oz) beer

salt and freshly ground black pepper

lemon wedges, to serve

1 Preheat the oven to Gas Mark 7/220°C/fan oven 200°C. Arrange the chips in a single layer on a non stick baking tray. Spray with the cooking spray and bake in the oven for 25–30 minutes, turning halfway until golden and crispy.

2 Meanwhile, arrange the cod fillets on another non stick baking tray. In a bowl, cream together the margarine, flour and bicarbonate of soda. Beat in the egg until smooth and then mix in the beer until a thick batter.

3 After 30 minutes, put the chips on to the lowest shelf in the oven. Spread the batter in a thick layer over the top of each cod fillet, trying not to let it go on the sides. Bake in the oven on a high shelf for 10–15 minutes, until puffed up and golden. Serve immediately with the chips and lemon wedges on the side.

Serving suggestion For the full experience, serve with 70 g (2½ oz) cooked peas per person, blended in a food processor, or using a hand blender, until mushy, along with grilled tomato halves. Enjoy with the remaining 250 ml (9 fl oz) from the beer bottle, for an extra 2 **POINTS** values per serving.

heavenly

beef Wellington pie

All the flavours of this classic dish are deliciously sealed under a crunchy filo pastry lid.

Serves 4

Takes *25 minutes to prepare + 30 minutes chilling, 30–40 minutes to cook*

23 *POINTS values per recipe*

332 calories *per serving*

goes well with...

The Roasted Nutty Chicory on page 176, for an extra 2 POINTS values per serving.

450 g (1 lb) lean fillet steak, cut into chunks

low fat cooking spray

1 red onion, chopped roughly

150 g (5½ oz) chestnut mushrooms, wiped and sliced thickly

1 tablespoon fresh thyme leaves

1 garlic clove, crushed

50 ml (2 fl oz) beef stock

75 g (2¾ oz) smooth wild mushroom pâté with Madeira

75 g (2¾ oz) low fat soft cheese

8 x 15 g sheets filo pastry

a few sprigs of fresh thyme, to garnish

1 Preheat the oven to Gas Mark 4/180°C/fan oven 160°C. Heat a non stick frying pan until hot and spray the steak with the cooking spray. Cook the steak in batches, for 5 minutes until browned. Remove and set aside.

2 Spray the pan again with the cooking spray and cook the onion, mushrooms and thyme for 3–4 minutes until softened. Add the garlic and cook for 1 minute. Then stir in the stock, pâté and soft cheese until smooth and combined. Remove the pan from the heat and return the steak, stirring to coat. Spoon into a 1.2 litre (2 pint) ovenproof dish and leave to cool for 30 minutes.

3 Scrunch the filo pastry, sheet by sheet, and arrange in a single layer over the top of the dish. Spray with the cooking spray and bake in the oven for 25–30 minutes until golden and bubbling. If you like your steak well done, cook for another 5–10 minutes. Serve immediately, garnished with the thyme.

Tip This recipe can be prepared up to 1 day in advance to the end of step 2 and then chilled in the fridge. Bring back to room temperature before finishing the dish.

pork cassoulet

A hearty, slow cooked bean stew from the South West of France. You can use different types of sausages, to replace the chipolatas, such as 100 g (3½ oz) chorizo, for 5½ POINTS values per serving.

❄ **Serves 4**

Takes *20 minutes to prepare, 30 minutes to cook*

23 POINTS *values per recipe*

334 calories *per serving*

450 g (1lb) pork tenderloin, cut into thick slices

low fat cooking spray

3 x 30 g (1¼ oz) chipolata sausages, each cut into 4 pieces

1 onion, chopped roughly

1 large carrot, peeled and sliced

2 celery sticks, sliced

125 ml (4 fl oz) dry white wine

150 ml (5 fl oz) chicken stock

300 g (10½ oz) passata

1 tablespoon dried herbes de Provence

1 x 410 g can cannellini beans in water, drained and rinsed

50 g (1¾ oz) ciabatta, cut into 4 slices

freshly ground black pepper

1 Preheat oven to Gas Mark 4/180°C/fan oven 160°C. Heat a flame and ovenproof lidded casserole dish. Spray the pork with the cooking spray. Cook for 5 minutes until browned. You may need to do this in batches. Remove and set aside. Add the chipolata pieces and cook for 3 minutes until brown. Remove and set aside.

2 Spray the casserole dish again with the cooking spray and cook the onion, carrot and celery for 5 minutes until starting to soften. Add the wine, stock, passata, dried herbs, cannellini beans and return the pork and chipolatas to the dish.

3 Bring to the boil, cover and then cook in the oven for 15 minutes. Remove from the oven and take off the lid. Lay the ciabatta slices on top, spray with the cooking spray and season with freshly ground black pepper. Return to the oven and bake uncovered for 15 minutes until golden.

Serving suggestion Serve with lots of steamed shredded cabbage or greens, for no extra **POINTS** values.

lemon chicken burger

6 POINTS VALUE

Burgers are the ultimate in comfort food and the whole family will love them. Fill the bun with lots of **lettuce**, sliced **gherkins**, **tomatoes** and **onion**, for no additional **POINTS** values.

❄ *chicken only*

Serves 4

Takes *20 minutes to prepare, 15 minutes to cook*

24½ POINTS *values per recipe*

379 calories *per serving*

4 x 125 g (4½ oz) skinless boneless chicken breasts

zest and juice of 2 lemons

125 g (4½ oz) natural dried breadcrumbs

2 tablespoons finely chopped fresh curly parsley

1 egg, beaten

1 tablespoon plain flour

low fat cooking spray

2 x 50 g ciabatta rolls, cut in half

1 teaspoon garlic purée

2 tablespoons reduced fat mayonnaise

2 tablespoons soured cream

1 tablespoon snipped fresh chives

1 Preheat the oven to Gas Mark 6/200°C/fan oven 180°C. Put a non stick baking tray in to heat. With each piece of chicken, make a large horizontal cut from the right side through the middle but leaving it still attached. Open up like a book. Put into a shallow dish and squeeze over the lemon juice. Set aside. In a separate shallow dish, mix together the breadcrumbs, lemon zest and parsley. Put the beaten egg in another dish, dust the chicken with the flour, dip it into the egg and then into the breadcrumbs, until coated all over.

2 Preheat the grill to hot. (If your grill is in your oven and not separate, toast the rolls first, before cooking the chicken.) Remove the baking tray from the oven, spray the chicken with the cooking spray and put on to the preheated baking tray. Cook the chicken in the oven for 12–15 minutes until golden.

3 Meanwhile, grill the ciabatta halves for 1-2 minutes. Combine the garlic, mayonnaise, soured cream and chives. Serve the chicken on a roll half, topped with mayonnaise

bolognese bake

This has to be the world's easiest adaptation of the favourite spaghetti bolognese.

 Serves 4

Takes *10 minutes to prepare, 45 minutes to cook*
25 POINTS *values per recipe*
378 calories *per serving*

½ onion, grated
2 garlic cloves, **crushed**
1 x 350 g pack vegetarian mince
1 x 400 g can chopped tomatoes
1 tablespoon dried oregano
1 tablespoon tomato purée
150 ml (5 fl oz) vegetable stock
125 g (4½ oz) fresh fusilli pasta
300 g (10½ oz) low fat soft cheese with garlic and herbs
2 egg yolks
salt and freshly ground black pepper

1 Preheat the oven to Gas Mark 4/180°C/fan oven 160°C. In a large bowl, mix together the onion, garlic, mince, tomatoes, oregano and tomato purée. Stir through the stock and pasta, then season. Spoon into a 1½ litre (2¾ pint) ovenproof dish.

2 Mix together the soft cheese, egg yolks and seasoning. Spread over the top of the pasta and mince. Bake in the oven for 40–45 minutes until golden and bubbling.

Meat variation You can use 400 g (14 oz) lean beef mince and cook in a non stick frying pan for 5 minutes until brown, breaking it into small pieces with a wooden spoon, before following the recipe as above from step 1, for 8 **POINTS** values per serving.

Italian classics

veggie sausage ragu

Ragu is a thick Italian sauce served with pasta. This is a great vegetarian version of a classic Italian sauce.

Ⓥ ❋ *the ragu sauce only*
Serves 4
Takes *35 minutes*
34 POINTS *values per recipe*
479 calories *per serving*

low fat cooking spray
1 onion, diced finely
1 x 250 g pack vegetarian sausages, chopped finely
350 g (12 oz) pasta shells
125 ml (4 fl oz) red wine
2 tablespoons tomato purée
300 ml (10 fl oz) vegetable stock
150 g (5½ oz) cherry tomatoes,
halved
75 g (2¾ oz) roasted red peppers in brine, drained, de-seeded and diced
a generous handful of fresh basil leaves
50 g (1¾ oz) vegetarian Parmesan cheese, grated
freshly ground black pepper

1 Bring a large saucepan of water to the boil. Meanwhile, heat a non stick saucepan and spray with the cooking spray. Cook the onion for 3–4 minutes until softened but not coloured. Spray the pan again with the cooking spray and add the sausages. Continue to cook for 5 minutes until starting to brown, stirring occasionally.

2 Add the pasta to the boiling water and cook for 10 minutes, or according to the packet instructions, until al dente. Meanwhile, add the wine to the sausage mix and bubble for 2 minutes, until reduced. Stir in the tomato purée and stock. Gently simmer for 10 minutes. Stir the tomatoes into the pan with the peppers and gently cook for 5 minutes until the tomatoes are beginning to soften. Season with freshly ground black pepper.

3 Drain the pasta. Return to the pan. Pour the sausage ragu into the pasta and stir to coat. Put into warmed bowls, scatter over the basil and top with the Parmesan.

Get ready to **feel full** with these fantastic one pot wonders. They're definitely the way forward if you're looking to keep **hunger at bay**. Sit back, relax and enjoy great food for less effort. Invest in a casserole dish and enjoy Braised Italian Chicken or Pot Roast for a different Sunday lunch, or try Oriental Pork Casserole as an alternative to the Chinese takeaway. Put your feet up and leave the delicious Chicken and Mushroom Hot Pot to just bubble away on the stove or bake in the oven while you chill out. Herby Chicken Casserole or White Pork Bourguignon are ideal for **easy entertaining** and they'll leave you more time with your guests. If you make these dishes the day before, the flavours are even more delicious the next day.

Roasted Vegetable Stew, page 108

vegetarian goulash

The key to this dish is to make sure all the vegetables are cut to the same size.

Ⓨ Serves 4
Takes *20 minutes*
1 POINTS *value per recipe*
102 calories *per serving*

low fat cooking spray
1 onion, chopped roughly
1 garlic clove, crushed
2 red or green peppers,
   de-seeded and cut into eighths
3 portabello mushrooms, wiped,
   trimmed and quartered
1 x 400 g can artichoke hearts
   in water, drained and quartered
1 tablespoon rose harissa
1 tablespoon paprika
1 tablespoon sun dried tomato
   paste
1 x 400 g can chopped tomatoes
300 ml (10 fl oz) vegetable stock
1 tablespoon finely chopped fresh
   flat leaf parsley, to garnish

1 Heat a large non stick saucepan and spray with the cooking spray. Add the onion and cook for 3–4 minutes until softened but not coloured. Add the garlic, peppers, mushrooms and artichokes and cook for 3 minutes until starting to brown.

2 Stir in the harissa, paprika and tomato paste and cook for 1 minute. Add the tomatoes and vegetable stock, bring to the boil and simmer for 10 minutes until thickened. Serve immediately in shallow bowls, scattered with parsley.

mulled Quorn pot

Sauerkraut is pickled cabbage and can be found with the pickled gherkins and onions in most supermarkets.

Ⓨ Serves 4
Takes *15 minutes to prepare,
15 minutes to cook*
4½ POINTS *values per recipe*
89 calories *per serving*

2 teaspoons Sichaun
   peppercorns
1 tablespoon fresh thyme leaves
4 x 51 g Quorn fillets
low fat cooking spray
1 red onion, sliced finely
2 red eating apples, peeled,
cored and each cut into eighths
½ x 810 g jar sauerkraut, drained
2 teaspoons vegetable gravy
   granules
300 ml (10 fl oz) hot vegetable
   stock
1 bag mulled wine spice

1 Crush the peppercorns lightly with a pestle and mortar. Put the crushed peppercorns and thyme on to a plate and press the Quorn fillets into the mixture to coat one side. Spray a large lidded non stick saucepan with the cooking spray and cook the Quorn fillets for 5 minutes until brown. Remove and set aside.

2 Spray the pan again with the cooking spray and cook the onion and apple for 3–4 minutes starting to brown. Add the sauerkraut, gravy granules and stock and stir lightly until the granules have dissolved. Empty the spices out of the mulled wine spice bag and into the pan, stirring until mixed.

3 Return the Quorn fillets nestling into the cabbage. Bring to the boil, cover tightly and simmer for 15 minutes until the apples are tender and the juices have thickened. Serve immediately.

roasted vegetable stew

Chunky veggies in a rich tomato sauce.

 Serves 2

Takes *10 minutes to prepare, 1 hour to cook*

3 POINTS *values per recipe*

229 calories *per serving*

1 garlic clove**, crushed**

1 red onion**, chopped roughly**

1 sweet potato **(about 250 g/9 oz), peeled and cut into wedges**

1 red pepper**, de-seeded and cut into chunks**

2 courgettes**, trimmed and cut into chunks**

low fat cooking spray

50 ml (2 fl oz) white balsamic vinegar

150 ml (5 fl oz) vegetable stock

250 ml (9 fl oz) passata

1 tablespoon dried herbes de Provence

a handful of fresh basil **leaves, to garnish**

salt and freshly ground black pepper

1 Preheat the oven to Gas Mark 6/200°C/fan oven 180°C. Put the garlic, onion, potato, pepper and courgettes into a deep ovenproof casserole dish. Spray with the cooking spray and pour in the balsamic vinegar. Toss to coat and then roast in the oven for 30 minutes until starting to char.

2 Pour in the stock, passata and dried herbs and cook in the oven for a further 30 minutes until tender and thickened. Check the seasoning, scatter over the basil and serve.

Serving suggestion Serve with 150 g (5½ oz) cooked brown rice per person, for an extra 3 **POINTS** values per serving.

Danish cod casserole

A fresh tasting and flavourful fish stew.

Serves 4

Takes *10 minutes to prepare, 20 minutes to cook*

8½ POINTS *values per recipe*

183 calories *per serving*

low fat cooking spray
1 onion, chopped finely
1 leek, rinsed and sliced thickly
1 teaspoon fennel seeds, crushed
   lightly
2 courgettes, grated coarsely
250 g (9 oz) potatoes, peeled and
   cubed
150 ml (5 fl oz) skimmed milk

300 ml (10 fl oz) fish stock
400 g (14 oz) cod loin fillets, cut
   into large chunks
2 tomatoes, de-seeded and diced
1 tablespoon finely chopped fresh
   curly parsley
zest of ¼ orange
salt and freshly ground black
   pepper

1 Heat a lidded non stick saucepan and spray with the cooking spray. Cook the onion, leek and fennel seeds for 5 minutes until softened but not coloured.

2 Add the courgettes, potatoes, milk and fish stock. Bring to the boil. Cover and gently simmer for 15 minutes until the potatoes are tender. Stir in the cod and simmer for 5 minutes until cooked.

3 Meanwhile, mix together the tomatoes, parsley and orange zest. Check the seasoning of the stew and serve in warmed bowls, topped with the diced tomato mixture.

Variation This also works really well with chunks of monkfish, for the same **POINTS** values.

winter mushrooms pot

Cooked chestnuts help to thicken this stew, but they also add a warming sweetness to the dish.

Ⓥ Serves 2

Takes *10 minutes to prepare, 30 minutes to cook*

3½ POINTS *values per recipe*

162 calories *per serving*

low fat cooking spray

1 small leek, sliced finely and rinsed

1 carrot, peeled and sliced

1 garlic clove, crushed

4 sprigs of fresh thyme

1 x 250 g pack small chestnut mushrooms, wiped, trimmed and halved

75 g (2¾ oz) whole, cooked, vacuum packed chestnuts, chopped roughly

2 teaspoons plain flour

50 ml (2 fl oz) marsala wine

400 ml (14 fl oz) vegetable stock

½ x 25 g pack dried mixed mushrooms

salt and freshly ground black pepper

1 Heat a large saucepan and spray with the cooking spray. Cook the leek and carrot for 3–4 minutes. Spray the pan again, and add the garlic, thyme, mushrooms and chestnuts. Cook for 2 minutes, stirring.

2 Sprinkle over the flour and then pour in the wine, stirring for 30 seconds. Gradually stir in the stock, then add the dried mushrooms and bring to the boil. Simmer gently for 30 minutes until thickened. Check the seasoning and serve immediately.

Serving suggestion Serve with 100 g (3½ oz) boiled potatoes per person and cooked green beans, for an extra 1 **POINTS** value per serving.

easy and warming

chick pea coconut stew

(3) POINTS VALUE

Serves 4
Takes *25 minutes*
12 POINTS *values per recipe*
165 calories *per serving*

low fat cooking spray
4 shallots, sliced finely
1 lemongrass stalk, outer leaves removed and sliced finely
1 small red chilli, de-seeded and diced finely
1 x 120 g pack shiitake mushrooms, trimmed and sliced
150 g (5½ oz) tenderstem broccoli, trimmed and halved
2 teaspoons cornflour
1 x 410 g can chick peas in water, drained and rinsed
150 g (5½ oz) Savoy cabbage, cored and shredded
600 ml (1 pint) vegetable stock
½ x 400 ml can reduced fat coconut milk

1 Heat a large saucepan and spray with the cooking spray. Cook the shallots, lemongrass and chilli for 2 minutes. Spray the pan again and stir in the mushrooms and broccoli. Cook for 3 minutes.

2 Stir in the cornflour, chick peas and cabbage. Gradually stir in the vegetable stock and coconut milk. Bring to a simmer and bubble for 10 minutes until thickened and tender. Spoon into warmed bowls and serve immediately.

Serving suggestion Enjoy this with a 50 g (1¾ oz) bread roll per person, to mop up the juices, for an additional 2 **POINTS** values per serving.

Moroccan spiced lamb

Scotch bonnet chillies are small and very hot. It is important to wear gloves, or to wash your hands thoroughly and avoid contact with your eyes after preparing.

Serves 4

Takes *25 minutes to prepare, 2 hours to cook*

13½ POINTS *values per recipe*

219 calories *per serving*

400 g (14 oz) lean boneless leg of lamb, **cut into large chunks**

low fat cooking spray

1 onion, **chopped roughly**

4 garlic cloves, **sliced**

1 red Scotch bonnet chilli, **de-seeded and sliced finely**

a generous pinch of saffron threads

1 x 400 g can chopped tomatoes

1 teaspoon smoked paprika

1 teaspoon ras el hanout

250 ml (9 fl oz) lamb stock

1 x 410 g can chick peas **in water, drained and rinsed**

2 tablespoons freshly chopped coriander

salt and freshly ground black pepper

1 Heat a large, lidded, heavy based saucepan and spray the lamb with the cooking spray. Cook the lamb for 5 minutes until brown all over. You may need to do this in batches. Remove and transfer to a plate. Add the onion to the pan and cook for 3–4 minutes until starting to soften. Add the garlic, chilli and saffron. Cook for 2 minutes, stirring.

2 Return the lamb to the pan and add the tomatoes, paprika, ras el hanout, stock and chick peas. Bring to the boil, cover and simmer for 2 hours until thickened and the lamb is tender. Check the seasoning, stir through the coriander and serve immediately.

Ⓥ Vegetarian option Instead of using the lamb, you can brown 1 large, cubed aubergine and 2 de-seeded and roughly chopped red peppers. Replace the lamb stock with vegetable stock and simmer for 1 hour in step 2, for 1 **POINTS** value per serving.

Tip If you don't like it hot, then simply use a large red chilli or serve with 1 tablespoon of **0% fat Greek yogurt** per person, for an added ½ **POINTS** value per serving.

chicken and mushroom hot pot

4 POINTS VALUE

Although you do need to use a frying pan as well, this layered dish takes moments to prepare, so you can sit back and relax while it cooks.

Serves 4
Takes *20 minutes to prepare,*
1¼ hours to cook
16½ POINTS *values per recipe*
288 calories *per serving*

4 x 150 g (5½ oz) skinless
   boneless chicken breasts,
   each cut into 3 pieces
low fat cooking spray
1 leek, **sliced finely and rinsed**
2 garlic cloves, **crushed**
1 x 250 g pack chestnut
   mushrooms, **wiped, trimmed**
   and halved

2 sprigs of fresh rosemary, **leaves**
   only
300 g (10½ oz) potatoes, **peeled**
   and sliced thinly
300 g (10½ oz) swede, **peeled**
   and sliced thinly
300 ml (10 fl oz) chicken stock
150 g (5½ oz) low fat soft cheese
salt and freshly ground black
   pepper

1 Preheat the oven to Gas Mark 5/190°C/fan oven 170°C. Heat a non stick frying pan and spray the chicken with the cooking spray. Cook the chicken pieces for 5 minutes until brown all over. Remove and transfer to a plate. Spray the pan again and cook the leek, garlic, mushrooms and rosemary for 5 minutes until softened. Remove from the heat.

2 Put half the chicken into a lidded 2 litre (3½ pint) ovenproof lidded casserole dish and cover with half the mushroom and leek mixture. Top with half the potatoes and swede and then repeat the layers, ending with potatoes.

3 Mix together the stock and soft cheese and pour over the potatoes. Cover and bake in the oven, for 30 minutes. Remove the lid and bake for a further 45 minutes until golden and the potatoes are tender. Serve immediately.

herby chicken casserole

Succulent chicken in a light creamy sauce, perfect as a midweek supper or as a meal with friends.

❄ **Serves 4**

Takes *25 minutes to prepare, 1 hour to cook*

15½ POINTS *values per recipe*

246 calories *per serving*

goes well with...

The Bacon and Onion Mash on page 181, for an extra 3 POINTS values per serving.

4 x 165 g (5¾ oz) skinless boneless chicken breasts

1 tablespoon finely chopped fresh tarragon

1 tablespoon finely chopped fresh parsley

1 tablespoon snipped fresh chives

low fat cooking spray

1 fennel bulb**, trimmed and chopped roughly**

150 g (5½ oz) small Chantenay carrots**, trimmed and scrubbed**

6 whole garlic cloves**, peeled**

300 ml (10 fl oz) chicken stock

200 g (7 oz) low fat soft cheese

freshly ground black pepper

1 Cut a pocket into the thickest part of each chicken breast. In a small bowl, mix together the tarragon, parsley, chives and freshly ground black pepper. Fill each chicken pocket with some of the herb mixture.

2 Heat a large lidded flameproof casserole dish and spray the chicken with the cooking spray. Cook the chicken for 5 minutes until browned all over. Remove and transfer to a plate.

3 Spray the casserole pan again with the cooking spray and cook the fennel, carrots and garlic for 5–7 minutes, stirring occasionally until starting to soften and colour. Return the chicken to the pan and pour in the chicken stock. Bring to the boil, cover and simmer for 1 hour.

4 Remove the chicken and vegetables from the pan using a slotted spoon and transfer to a warm plate. Whisk the soft cheese into the pan and bring to the boil. Bubble for 5–8 minutes until slightly reduced and thickened. Check the seasoning, return the chicken and vegetables to the pan to warm and serve immediately.

Serving suggestion Serve with cooked sugar snap peas, mange tout and broccoli, for no extra **POINTS** values per serving.

Oriental pork casserole

Black beans *have a distinctive sweet flavour when cooked and are available dried from most large supermarkets.*

❄ **Serves 4**
Takes *20 minutes to prepare + overnight soaking, 1½ hours to cook*
15 POINTS *values per recipe*
262 calories *per serving*

60 g (2 oz) dried black beans, **covered with cold water and soaked overnight**
600 g (1 lb 5 oz) boneless pork shoulder steaks, **cut into chunks**
30 g (1¼ oz) fresh ginger, peeled and sliced thinly
2 red chillies, **de-seeded and sliced**
3 garlic cloves, **sliced**
2 star anise
1 teaspoon Thai 7 spice
1 onion, **chopped roughly**
75 ml (3 fl oz) soy sauce
150 ml (5 fl oz) chicken stock
1 x 25 g pack fresh coriander, **leaves only**

1 Drain and rinse the black beans which have been soaking overnight, then put them in a saucepan and cover with cold water. Bring to the boil and rapidly boil for 10 minutes. Drain and rinse again. Meanwhile, off the heat, put the pork, ginger, chillies, garlic, star anise, Thai 7 spice and onion into a large lidded flameproof casserole dish. Mix everything together.

2 Add the black beans and pour in the soy sauce and chicken stock. Put on to the heat and bring to the boil. Cover and simmer for 1½ hours, stirring occasionally until tender. Serve in shallow bowls, topped with the coriander leaves.

Serving suggestion Serve with 40 g (1½ oz) dried noodles per person, cooked according to packet instructions, and with plenty of steamed pak choi, for an additional 2 **POINTS** values per serving.

Variation If you can't find dried black beans or are short of time, why not use a 410 g can of aduki beans (drained and rinsed), instead of the black beans, for the same **POINTS** values per serving.

pot roast

Soaking the shallots in boiling
water makes them easier to
peel.

Serves 6

Takes *25 minutes to prepare,
2 hours to cook*

22½ POINTS *values per
recipe*

246 calories *per serving*

goes well with...

**The Roasted Root
Vegetables on page 174,
followed by the Orange
Panna cotta on page 191,
for an extra 3½ POINTS
values per serving.**

250 g (9 oz) small shallots

700 g (1 lb 9 oz) lean silverside
  of beef

6 x 15 g (½ oz) Parma ham **slices**

low fat cooking spray

2 large garlic cloves

6 small sprigs of fresh rosemary

2 tablespoons tomato purée

450 ml (16 fl oz) beef stock

1 x 25 g pack dried porcini
  mushrooms

2 sprigs of fresh thyme

1 x 420 g can butter beans,
  drained and rinsed

1 Preheat the oven to Gas Mark 3/160°C/fan oven 140°C. Put the shallots in a bowl. Cover with boiling water. Set aside. Wrap the beef in the ham and spray with the cooking spray. Heat a large, lidded oven and flameproof casserole dish. Cook the beef for 5 minutes, turning until brown all over. Remove and set aside to cool.

2 Cut each garlic clove into six slivers. Make about twelve deep cuts into the top of the beef and fill each with a sliver of garlic and a small sprig of rosemary.

3 Drain and peel the shallots. Halve any that are large. Heat the casserole dish again and spray with the cooking spray. Cook the shallots for 5 minutes until starting to soften and brown. Stir in the tomato purée and cook for 30 seconds. Stir in the stock, dried mushrooms, thyme and butter beans.

4 Return the beef, nestling it into the beans. Bring to the boil, cover and then cook in the oven for 2 hours. To serve, remove the beef and carve it into slices, dividing it equally between the six plates. Spoon over the vegetables and pan juices.

braised Italian chicken

Limoncello is an Italian lemon liqueur and when simmered slowly gives the chicken a zesty sweet sauce.

Serves 4

Takes *35 minutes to prepare,*
1½ hours to cook

18 POINTS *values per recipe*
330 calories *per serving*

goes well with...

The Parisienne Potatoes on page 183, for an extra 3½ POINTS values per serving.

1 x 1.5 kg (3 lb 5 oz) whole chicken

low fat cooking spray

3 garlic cloves, halved horizontally

1 onion, chopped roughly

2 small fennel bulbs, trimmed and cut into chunks

2 parsnips (total 180 g), peeled and cut into chunks

5 preserved lemons from a jar, drained and halved

4 sprigs of fresh thyme, plus extra to garnish

450 ml (16 fl oz) chicken stock

125 ml (4 fl oz) limoncello

freshly ground black pepper

1 Heat a large, lidded flameproof casserole dish until hot and spray the chicken with the cooking spray. Brown the chicken for 5–8 minutes, turning until brown on all sides. Remove and set aside. Spray the pan with the cooking spray and add the garlic, onion, fennel and parsnips. Gently cook for 8–10 minutes until starting to soften and browned.

2 Put half the preserved lemons and sprigs of thyme into the chicken cavity. Return the chicken to the casserole dish and scatter over the remaining lemons. Pour over the chicken stock and limoncello. Bring to the boil. Cover with foil, then cover with the lid and gently simmer for 1½ hours until the chicken is cooked.

3 To serve, remove the chicken from the dish and cover loosely with foil to rest. Using a slotted spoon, remove the vegetables and keep warm. Bring the cooking liquid to the boil and rapidly bubble for 5–10 minutes until reduced by half and thickened. Check the seasoning and pour into a jug. Allow it to settle, then spoon off any fat. Remove the chicken skin and discard, carve the chicken into slices and serve 120 g (4½ oz) per person with the vegetables and sauce. Garnish with thyme and freshly ground black pepper.

white pork bourguignon

Make sure you use a good
white wine from Burgundy to
really make this dish special.

❄ **Serves 4**
Takes 25 minutes to prepare,
2 hours to cook
20 POINTS values per recipe
326 calories per serving

goes well with...
**The Chocolate
Marshmallow Meringue
Cake on page 199, for an
extra 3½ POINTS values
per serving.**

1 tablespoon plain flour
750 g (1 lb 10 oz) boneless pork shoulder**, cut into 5 cm (2 inch) pieces**
low fat cooking spray
1 onion**, chopped finely**
1 garlic clove**, crushed**
200 g (7 oz) chestnut mushrooms**, wiped and trimmed**
½ celeriac **(about 350 g/12 oz), peeled and cut into bite size cubes**
300 ml (10 fl oz) white burgundy wine
300 ml (10 fl oz) chicken stock
1 dried bouquet garni
4 sprigs of fresh thyme
salt and freshly ground black pepper

1 Put the flour on to a plate and dust the pork in it, shaking off the excess. Heat a lidded, flameproof casserole dish and spray with the cooking spray. Cook the pork for 5 minutes, turning until brown all over. You may need to do this in batches. Remove and set aside.

2 Add the onion, garlic, mushrooms and celeriac to the pan and cook gently for 5 minutes until starting to brown. Return the pork and pour in the wine, chicken stock, bouquet garni and thyme. Bring to the boil, cover and simmer for 2 hours until the pork is tender and the juices have thickened. Remove the bouquet garni. Check the seasoning and serve.

Serving suggestion Serve with a 125 g (2½ oz) scoop of mashed potato (made up with 1 tablespoon skimmed milk) per person and 35 g (1¼ oz) cooked broad beans per person, for an extra 2 **POINTS** values per serving.

braised rosemary and lentil lamb

You may need to cook the lentils in a separate pan but then everything goes into one pot to cook.

Serves 4

Takes *25 minutes to prepare, 1½ hours to cook*

21 POINTS *values per recipe*

236 calories *per serving*

75 g (2¾ oz) puy lentils, washed

1 tablespoon plain flour

4 x 150 g (5½ oz) lean lamb leg steaks

low fat cooking spray

1 x 280 g jar silverskin onions in vinegar, drained and rinsed

2 garlic cloves, sliced

3 sprigs of fresh rosemary

75 ml (3 fl oz) ruby Port

300 ml (10 fl oz) lamb stock

1 tablespoon redcurrant jelly

salt and freshly ground black pepper

1 Preheat the oven to Gas Mark 3/160°C/fan oven 140°C. Put the lentils into a saucepan and cover with cold water. Bring to the boil and simmer for 5 minutes. Drain and rinse in cold water.

2 Meanwhile, put the flour on to a plate and dust the lamb steaks in it, shaking off the excess. Heat a lidded flame and ovenproof casserole dish and spray the lamb with the cooking spray. Cook the lamb for 5 minutes, turning until brown all over. Remove and set aside.

3 Add the onions, garlic and rosemary and cook gently for 3 minutes until starting to brown. Add the Port, stock, redcurrant jelly and drained lentils and return the lamb.

4 Bring to the boil, cover and cook in the oven for 1½ hours until the juices have reduced and the lamb is tender. Check the seasoning, remove the sprigs of rosemary and serve immediately.

Serving suggestion Serve with 100 g (3½ oz) potatoes per person, cubed and sautéed in low fat cooking spray, as well as cooked, fine green beans, for 1 extra **POINTS** value per serving.

steak and ginger wine hot pot

Cooking beef slowly in the oven on a low heat makes it so tender it literally melts in the mouth. For the best flavour, make this the day before, and then gently heat until hot.

❄ **Serves 4**

Takes *35 minutes to prepare, 2 hours to cook*

22 POINTS *values per recipe*

316 calories *per serving*

250 g (9 oz) shallots
½ kettle boiling water, to cover the shallots
1 tablespoon plain flour
500 g (1 lb 2 oz) lean stewing beef, **cut into large cubes**
low fat cooking spray
2 garlic cloves, **crushed**
2 large carrots, **peeled and cut into thick batons**
325 g (11½ oz) swede, **peeled and cut into thick batons**
300 ml (10 fl oz) ginger wine
300 ml (10 fl oz) beef stock
2 tablespoons tomato purée
2 bay leaves
salt and freshly ground black pepper

1 Preheat the oven to Gas Mark 4/180°C/fan oven 160°C. Put the shallots in a bowl and cover with the boiling water (this makes them easier to peel). Set aside. Meanwhile, put the flour on to a plate and dust the beef in it, shaking off the excess. Heat a lidded flame and ovenproof casserole dish and spray with the cooking spray. Cook the beef for 5 minutes, turning until brown all over. You may need to do this in batches. Remove and set aside.

2 Drain the shallots and then peel and trim. Heat the casserole pan again and add the shallots, garlic, carrots and swede. Cook gently for 5–8 minutes until starting to brown. Return the beef to the pan and pour in the ginger wine, beef stock, tomato purée and bay leaves. Bring to the boil, cover and cook in the oven for 2 hours until tender and the juices have reduced and thickened. Remove the bay leaf, check the seasoning and serve.

Serving suggestion Serve with a 125 g (4½ oz) scoop of mashed potato (made with 1 tablespoon of skimmed milk) per person and cooked tenderstem broccoli, for an extra 1½ **POINTS** values per serving.

If seafood is your passion, look no further than these lovely recipes. They're also great value for your **POINTS** allowance. Impress your guests with Baked Prawn Risotto and Salmon and Potato Tart or indulge in Garlicky Mussels Gratin and White Pepper Prawns for the perfect light bite. Prepare a fishy feast with the comforting Italian Seafood Stew or fire up the barbecue and get cooking Spiced Cod Kebabs. But enjoying fish doesn't have to be expensive - with a few clever store cupboard ingredients, you can whip up Zesty Tuna Spaghetti in moments.

Pan-Fried Chilli Scallops, *page 126*

spiced cod kebabs

These are perfect for the barbecue too.

❄ *raw marinated cod only*
Serves 4
Takes *20 minutes +*
30 minutes marinating,
10 minutes to cook
5½ POINTS *values per recipe*
110 calories *per serving*

goes well with...
The Creamy Potato Salad on page 176, for an extra 2 POINTS values per serving.

15 g (½ oz) **fresh ginger, peeled and grated**
1 **garlic clove, crushed**
zest and juice of a lime
a generous pinch of dried chilli flakes

1 tablespoon **finely chopped fresh mint**
1 teaspoon **ground turmeric**
450 g (1 lb) **cod loin fillets, cut into large chunks**
2 **courgettes, cut into chunks**
low fat cooking spray

1 In a non metallic bowl, mix together the ginger, garlic, lime zest and juice, chilli flakes and mint. In a separate bowl, add the turmeric and cod and toss to coat. Add to the ginger marinade, toss to coat and set aside for 30 minutes.

2 Preheat the grill to medium. Alternating chunks of courgette and cod, thread them on to four metal or wooden skewers. Place the skewers on a grill pan, spray with the cooking spray and cook for 8–10 minutes, turning occasionally until cooked. Serve immediately.

Serving suggestion Serve with 125 g (4½ oz) cooked corn on the cob per person, for an extra 1 POINTS value per serving.

pan-fried chilli scallops

Serves 2
Takes *25 minutes*
2½ POINTS *values per recipe*
92 calories *per serving*

low fat cooking spray
2 **garlic cloves, chopped finely**
2 **red chillies, de-seeded and diced finely**
1 **fennel bulb, diced finely**
200 g (7 oz) **scallops, cleaned and coral removed**

zest and juice of a lime
2 tablespoons **freshly chopped coriander**
1 tablespoon **fresh lemon thyme leaves**
salt and freshly ground black pepper

1 Heat a wide, lidded, non stick pan until hot and spray with the cooking spray. Cook the garlic, chilli and fennel for 2 minutes until starting to soften. Add 2 tablespoons of cold water, cover and sweat for 8–10 minutes. Transfer to a bowl and cover with foil.

2 Reheat the pan and spray again with the cooking spray. Add the scallops and cook for 5 minutes, turning halfway. Add the lime zest and juice, coriander, thyme and fennel mixture and toss to coat. Check the seasoning and serve immediately.

Serving suggestion Toss the scallops through 40 g (1½ oz) dried tagliatelle per person, cooked according to packet instructions, for an additional 2 POINTS values per serving.

1½ POINTS VALUE

a refreshing taste
of the sea

white pepper prawns

This prawn cocktail is ideal for a light supper.

Serves 2

Takes 15 minutes + 30 minutes marinating

5½ POINTS values per recipe

168 calories per serving

1 tablespoon finely chopped fresh coriander

½ teaspoon ground white pepper

1 garlic clove, crushed

1 teaspoon Thai fish sauce

zest and juice of a lemon

200 g (7 oz) raw peeled tiger prawns

½ avocado, peeled, stoned and chopped roughly

50 g (1¾ oz) low fat natural yogurt

2 Little Gem lettuces, trimmed and leaves separated

1. In a non metallic bowl, mix together the coriander, white pepper, garlic, fish sauce, half the lemon zest and juice and prawns. Set aside for 30 minutes. Meanwhile, blend the avocado, yogurt and remaining lemon zest and juice in a food processor, or using a hand blender, until smooth.
2. Heat a griddle pan or non stick frying pan until hot and cook the prawns for 3–5 minutes, turning until pink and cooked through.
3. Divide the lettuce leaves between two plates and top each with a spoonful of avocado mixture. Top each with half the prawns and serve immediately.

Serving suggestion Serve with 150 g (5½ oz) cooked new potatoes per person, for an additional 1½ **POINTS** values per serving.

Italian seafood stew

This would also make a great starter for 8, for 1 POINTS value per serving.

Serves 4

Takes 15 minutes to prepare, 35 minutes to cook

9½ POINTS values per recipe

216 calories per serving

low fat cooking spray

1 onion, chopped finely

2 celery sticks, sliced finely

2 carrots, peeled and sliced thickly

100 g (3½ oz) dried macaroni pasta

600 ml (1 pint) fish stock

2 bay leaves

1 large preserved lemon from a jar, drained and sliced

1 x 400 g can chopped tomatoes

1 x 400 g (14 oz) frozen mixed seafood, such as squid, mussels and prawns

1 tablespoon chopped fresh dill

salt and freshly ground black pepper

1. Heat a lidded non stick saucepan and spray with the cooking spray. Cook the onion, celery and carrots for 5–8 minutes until beginning to soften but not brown.
2. Stir in the pasta, fish stock, bay leaves, lemon slices and tomatoes. Bring to the boil. Cover and gently simmer for 30 minutes until the pasta is cooked. Stir in the seafood and cook for 5 minutes more. Check the seasoning, remove the bay leaves and serve in warmed bowls sprinkled with the dill.

chilli and ginger glazed cod

Serves 2

Takes *15 minutes*

5½ *POINTS values per recipe*

205 calories per serving

1 tablespoon cornflour

2 tablespoons light soy sauce

15 g (½ oz) fresh ginger, peeled and shredded

1 tablespoon caster sugar

1 red chilli, de-seeded and sliced finely

2 teaspoons Thai fish sauce

4 tablespoons white wine vinegar

300 g (10½ oz) cod loin fillets, skinless and cut into chunks

low fat cooking spray

1 tablespoon fresh mint leaves

2 tablespoons freshly chopped coriander

1 Dissolve 1 teaspoon of cornflour in the soy sauce. Set aside. Put the ginger, sugar chilli, fish sauce, vinegar and 200 ml (7 fl oz) water into a small pan. Bring to the boil and rapidly bubble for 3–4 minutes. Stir in the soy sauce mixture and bubble for 1 minute more until thickened.

2 Meanwhile, coat the cod chunks in the remaining cornflour. Heat a non stick frying pan until hot and spray with the cooking spray. Cook the cod fillets for 5 minutes until golden and crispy, turning halfway through. Divide the cod between the bowls, pour over the sauce and top with the mint and coriander.

Serving suggestion This is ideal with 150 g (5½ oz) cooked brown rice per person and zero **POINTS** values stir fried vegetables, for an extra 3 **POINTS** values per serving.

Variation Try using 2 x 165 g (5¾ oz) diced, skinless boneless chicken breasts instead of the cod, for 3½ **POINTS** values per serving.

garlicky mussels gratin

3 POINTS VALUE

Green lipped mussels from New Zealand are plump and juicy. You can buy them already cooked from most fish counters in the supermarket.

Serves 2
Takes *10 minutes to prepare,*
10 minutes to cook
6 POINTS *values per recipe*
222 calories *per serving*

25 g (1 oz) herb foccacia, torn roughly
2 garlic cloves, chopped finely
250 g (9 oz) half shell cooked New Zealand green lipped mussels
  (about 12)
2 tomatoes, de-seeded and diced finely
3 tablespoons dry white wine
low fat cooking spray

1 Preheat the oven to Gas Mark 6/200°C/fan oven 180°C. Blend the foccacia and garlic in a food processor, or use a blender, until coarse breadcrumbs. Set aside. Arrange the mussels in a shallow ovenproof dish in a single layer, mussels facing upwards.

2 Scatter over the tomatoes and then drizzle over the white wine. Scatter over the foccacia crumbs, spray with the cooking spray and bake in the oven for 10 minutes until golden and bubbling hot.

Serving suggestion Serve with a 50 g (1¾ oz) bread roll each, for an extra 2 **POINTS** values per serving.

tuna with grape salsa

*This warm salsa is perfect
with fresh griddled tuna.*

Serves 4
Takes *30 minutes*
15 *POINTS* values per recipe
223 calories *per serving*

125 ml (4 fl oz) dry white wine

2 teaspoons caster sugar

1 teaspoon Dijon mustard

100 g (3½ oz) white seedless grapes, chopped finely

1 celery stick, diced finely

50 g (1¾ oz) stoned kalamata olives, chopped finely

1 tablespoon finely chopped fresh parsley

1 tablespoon snipped fresh chives

4 x 125 g (4½ oz) tuna steaks

low fat cooking spray

freshly ground black pepper

1 Put the wine and sugar into a small saucepan and bring to the boil. Simmer for 5 minutes until reduced. Stir in the mustard, grapes, celery, olives, parsley and chives. Season with freshly ground black pepper and set aside.

2 Meanwhile, heat a griddle pan or non stick frying pan until hot and spray the tuna steaks with the cooking spray. Cook for 6 minutes, turning halfway until cooked to your liking. Leave to rest for 5 minutes, then serve with the grape salsa.

Serving suggestion Serve with 150 g (5½ oz) cooked **polenta** per person and **mange tout**, for an extra 3 *POINTS* values per serving.

make it special

haddock kiev

1 heaped teaspoon garlic purée
1 tablespoon finely chopped fresh curly parsley
1 tablespoon snipped fresh chives
50 g (1¾ oz) low fat polyunsaturated margarine
4 x 125 g (4½ oz) skinless haddock loins
8 x 15 g (½ oz) slices Parma ham
freshly ground black pepper

If the fish is really fresh, this can be prepared a day in advance, then all that's left to do is pop them in the oven.

❄ *fish only, while still raw and up to the end of step 2*

Serves 4

Takes *10 minutes to prepare, 15 minutes to cook*

15 POINTS *values per recipe*

228 calories *per serving*

1 Preheat the oven to Gas Mark 5/190°C/fan oven 170°C. In a small bowl, mix together the garlic purée, parsley, chives, margarine and freshly ground black pepper.

2 Put the haddock loins on a board and cut each in half. Spread the garlic butter over four halves. Top each with another piece of haddock, sandwiching the garlic spread.

3 Wrap each haddock sandwich with two slices of Parma ham to enclose the fish. Transfer to a baking tray and roast in the oven for 10–15 minutes until golden and cooked. Serve immediately.

Serving suggestion Serve with a 225 g (8 oz) potato each, cut into wedges and baked in a hot oven until crispy, 35 g cooked peas per person and cooked asparagus spears, for an extra 3 POINTS values per serving.

skate with parsley sauce

Serves 4

Takes 10 minutes to prepare,
25 minutes to cook

19 POINTS values per recipe

297 calories per serving

goes well with...

The Tropical Tart on page 192, for an extra 2 POINTS values per serving.

low fat cooking spray

4 x 250 g (9 oz) skate wings

zest and juice of a lemon

3 x 15 g (½ oz) wholewheat crispbreads

1 x 200 g tub low fat soft cheese

4 tablespoons finely chopped fresh curly parsley

1 egg yolk

200 ml (7 fl oz) skimmed milk

freshly ground black pepper

1 Preheat the oven to Gas Mark 4/180°C/fan oven 160°C and spray an ovenproof dish with the cooking spray. Put the skate wings into the dish, trying not to overlap the wings, and pour over the lemon juice. Whizz the crispbreads in a food processor, until they are nearly fine crumbs and then sprinkle over the skate. Spray with the cooking spray and bake in the oven for 25 minutes.

2 Meanwhile, in a small saucepan, gently heat the soft cheese, lemon zest, parsley, egg yolk and lots of black pepper until starting to melt. Remove from the heat and gradually pour in the milk, whisking as you do, until smooth. Return to the heat and continue to heat until just simmering. Do not boil or over heat otherwise it will split. Serve the skate wings with the parsley sauce immediately.

Serving suggestion Serve with 150 g (5½ oz) cooked new potatoes per person and green beans and carrots, for an extra 1½ POINTS values per serving.

crispy salmon on creamy greens

Sprinkling spice on to skinless salmon before cooking gives the fish a crunchy crust.

Serves 2
Takes *15 minutes*
10 *POINTS values per recipe*
291 *calories per serving*

½ teaspoon cayenne pepper

2 x 125 g (4½ oz) skinless salmon fillets

low fat cooking spray

1 courgette, trimmed

1 garlic clove, sliced

100 g (3½ oz) baby spinach leaves

75 g (2¾ oz) low fat soft cheese

15 g (½ oz) capers in brine, drained and rinsed

2 tablespoons finely chopped fresh flat leaf parsley

zest of ½ a lemon, plus wedges to serve

salt and freshly ground black pepper

1 Put the cayenne pepper on to a plate and dip in each salmon fillet, pressing down gently to coat on one side. Heat a non stick frying pan until hot and spray the salmon with the cooking spray. Cook for 3 minutes, pepper side down, then flip over and cook for 2 minutes. Remove from the heat, wrap the salmon in foil and set aside.

2 Meanwhile, using a potato peeler, cut the courgette into ribbons. Spray the frying pan again with the cooking spray and cook the garlic, courgette ribbons and spinach for 2 minutes. Stir in the soft cheese and 3 tablespoons of cold water until smooth and the spinach is wilted.

3 Remove from the heat and stir through the capers, parsley, lemon zest and seasoning. Unwrap the salmon and serve immediately with the wilted creamy greens and lemon wedges.

Serving suggestion Serve with 150 g (5½ oz) diced potatoes per person, sautéed in low fat cooking spray and baby carrots, for an extra 1½ *POINTS* values per serving.

zesty tuna spaghetti

zest and juice of a lemon
150 g (5½ oz) dried spaghetti
1 x 200 g can tuna steak in brine, **drained**
4 tomatoes, **de-seeded and diced**
50 g (1¾ oz) roasted red pepper **from a jar, drained and diced**
1 tablespoon fresh oregano **leaves**
freshly ground black pepper

1 Put the lemon juice into a large pan and top up with enough cold water to fill the pan, about 1 litre. Bring to the boil, add the spaghetti and cook according to the packet instructions until al dente. Using a ladle, remove about 50 ml (2 fl oz) cooking liquid and reserve. Drain the spaghetti and leave to drain in the colander.
2 Meanwhile, put the tuna, lemon zest, tomatoes and peppers in the spaghetti pan with the reserved cooking liquid. Bring back to a simmer then stir in the spaghetti until combined and heated through.
3 Generously season with freshly ground black pepper and stir through the oregano. Serve immediately.

herring caesar salad

2 Romaine lettuce hearts, **cored and sliced thickly**
125 g (4½ oz) cucumber, **sliced thinly**
3 celery sticks, **sliced thickly**
5 tablespoons low fat Caesar dressing
1 avocado, **peeled, stoned and cubed**
50 g (1¾ oz) grated Parmesan cheese
1 egg white
50 g (1¾ oz) fresh breadcrumbs
1 teaspoon mild chilli powder
3 x 100 g (3½ oz) herring cutlets **or fillets**
low fat cooking spray
1 lemon, cut into wedges, to serve

1 Put the lettuce, cucumber and celery in a large salad bowl. Lightly toss with half the dressing. Divide between four plates and top with the avocado. Drizzle with the remaining dressing and scatter over the Parmesan cheese.
2 In a shallow, clean and grease-free bowl, lightly whisk the egg white. Put the breadcrumbs and chilli powder into another shallow bowl. Cut each herring fillet in half and then in half again to make 12 pieces. Dip the pieces, skin side only, into the egg white and then into the breadcrumbs until the skin is coated.
3 Heat a non stick frying pan and spray the fillets with the cooking spray. Breadcrumb side down, cook the fillets gently for 2 minutes until golden and then turn over and cook for another 2–3 minutes until cooked. Serve three pieces of herring on top of each salad with the lemon wedges on the side.

salmon and potato tart

This filling tart is delicious hot or cold.

Serves 4

Takes *40 minutes*

25 *POINTS* values per recipe

335 calories *per serving*

300 g (10½ oz) waxy potatoes such as Charlotte, peeled and cut into
    5 mm slices
1 x 100 g pack asparagus tips, trimmed
8 x 15 g sheets filo pastry
low fat cooking spray
2 tablespoons hot horseradish sauce
125 ml (4 fl oz) soured cream
250 g (9 oz) skinless salmon fillets, cut into 1 cm (¼ inch) thick slices
salt and freshly ground black pepper

1 Preheat the oven to Gas Mark 6/200°C/fan oven 180°C. Put the potato slices into a large saucepan and cover with cold water. Bring to the boil and simmer for 5 minutes. Add the asparagus for the last minute and simmer. Drain, rinse in cold water and dry between sheets of kitchen paper.

2 Meanwhile, lay a sheet of filo pastry on to a non stick baking tray and spray with the cooking spray. Take another filo sheet and lay it next to the other sheet, overlapping one long edge slightly to make a rectangle measuring 30 cm x 25 cm (12 inches x 10 inches). Spray again and repeat the layering until all the sheets are used.

3 Arrange the potato slices in a single layer, overlapping each other slightly on top of the filo rectangle, leaving a 2½ cm (1 inch) border all the way around. Spray the exposed filo pastry with the cooking spray and fold the pastry over the potato slightly to make a case. Bake in the oven for 10 minutes.

4 Meanwhile, in a bowl, mix together the horseradish sauce and soured cream. Remove the tart from the oven and spread the horseradish cream over the potato slices. Top with the salmon slices and asparagus tips and bake in the oven for 5–10 minutes until cooked. Cut into wedges and serve.

Serving suggestion Serve with a generous zero *POINTS* value salad, drizzled with 1 tablespoon of light salad cream and 1 tablespoon of reduced fat coleslaw per person, for an extra 1½ *POINTS* values per serving.

Ⓨ Vegetarian option You can replace the salmon with another 100 g pack of asparagus tips, for 4 *POINTS* values per serving.

6½ POINTS VALUE®

baked prawn risotto

This stress free risotto is so easy.

Serves 4

Takes *10 minutes to prepare, 30 minutes to cook*

25½ *POINTS values per recipe*

292 calories *per serving*

goes well with...

The Watercress and Asparagus Soup as a starter on page 30, for no extra *POINTS* values per serving.

low fat cooking spray

1 onion, **chopped finely**

2 garlic cloves, **chopped**

200 g (7 oz) **dried Arborio risotto rice**

75 ml (3 fl oz) **dry Martini**

50 ml (2 fl oz) **Pernod**

600 ml (1 pint) **hot fish stock**

200 g (7 oz) **peeled raw** king **prawns**

100 g (3½ oz) **peeled and cooked** prawns

½ x 290 g **jar marinated artichoke antipasti, drained and quartered**

zest of a lemon

2 tablespoons **finely chopped fresh** curly parsley

salt and freshly ground black pepper

1 Preheat the oven to Gas Mark 4/180°C/fan oven 160°C. Heat a non stick frying pan and spray with the cooking spray. Cook the onion for 3–4 minutes until softened but not coloured. Add the garlic and cook for 1 minute. Stir in the rice, then pour in the Martini and Pernod and allow it to bubble for 30–60 seconds. Transfer the mixture to a roasting pan and pour in the fish stock.

2 Bake in the oven for 20–25 minutes until nearly tender and the juices have been absorbed. Remove from the oven and stir in the king prawns and cooked prawns, artichoke hearts, lemon zest and season.

3 Cook in the oven for a further 5 minutes until the prawns are cooked. Check the seasoning, stir through the parsley and serve immediately.

hot mackerel salad

If making this ahead, don't add the beetroot until the last minute, otherwise everything will turn pink.

Serves 2

Takes *10 minutes*

12½ *POINTS values per recipe*

420 calories *per serving*

1 x 410 g **can** butter beans, **drained and rinsed**

2 tablespoons **finely chopped fresh** curly parsley

2 spring onions, **sliced finely**

75 g (2¾ oz) roasted red peppers **from a jar, drained and sliced finely**

1 tablespoon **reduced fat mayonnaise**

1 tablespoon **hot horseradish sauce**

zest of ½ a lemon

125 g (4½ oz) **smoked** mackerel fillets, **skin removed and flaked**

50 g (1¾ oz) **cooked** beetroot in natural juice, **diced**

30 g (1¼ oz) wild rocket

salt and freshly ground black pepper

1 Put the butter beans, parsley, spring onions, peppers, mayonnaise, horseradish and lemon zest in a bowl. Season.

2 Fold through the mackerel and beetroot. Serve immediately with the rocket.

Whether you're a meat-lover or a vegetarian, you'll find these delicious dishes inspiring. All of them are low in **POINTS** values and will keep you **satisfied for longer**. With veggie versions of classics such as Cottage Pie and Spicy Spinach Cannelloni or contemporary quick fixes like Chilli Tofu Noodles and Minestrone Salad, 'going green' has never tasted so good. If you need some **new ideas** for vegetables, look no further than foolproof dinners such as Mushroom Pilaff, Spinach Gnocchi Gratin and Spiced Parsnip Bake - so enjoy discovering the wonderful world of vegetables.

Crunchy Courgette Fritters, *page 153*

warm roasted squash salad

1½ POINTS VALUE

This autumnal salad makes the most of the sweet butternut squash flesh, but you can use other varieties such as *pumpkin*, for the same *POINTS* values per serving.

Ⓥ **Serves 4**

Takes *15 minutes to prepare, 1 hour to cook*

6½ POINTS *values per recipe*

180 calories *per serving*

700 g (1 lb 9 oz) butternut squash, peeled, de-seeded and cut into wedges

a generous pinch of dried chilli flakes

1 teaspoon coriander seeds, crushed lightly

2 tablespoons balsamic vinegar

low fat cooking spray

1 x 85 g bag wild rocket

1 x 410 g can chick peas in water, drained and rinsed

1 red onion, sliced

½ pomegranate, seeds removed and reserved

60 g (2 oz) low fat soft cheese with garlic and herbs

2 tablespoons skimmed milk

juice of ½ a lemon

1 Preheat the oven to Gas Mark 6/200°C/fan oven 180°C. Put the squash in a bowl and toss together with the chilli flakes, coriander seeds and balsamic vinegar. Tip on to a non stick baking tray and spray with the cooking spray. Roast in the oven for 45 minutes – 1 hour until roasted and tender.

2 Meanwhile, divide the rocket, chick peas, onion and pomegranate seeds between four plates.

3 In a bowl, mix together the soft cheese, skimmed milk and lemon juice. Divide the roasted squash between the salad plates and drizzle with the dressing.

spiced parsnip bake

This warming dish is a great way to use up leftovers too: simply mash equal quantities of cooked potatoes and vegetables and prepare from step 2.

Serves 4

Takes 25 minutes to prepare, 35 minutes to cook

8½ **POINTS** values per recipe

176 **calories** per serving

low fat cooking spray

250 g (9 oz) floury potatoes, peeled and cut into even chunks

350 g (12 oz) parsnips, peeled and cut into even chunks

½ small Savoy cabbage, outer leaves removed, cored and shredded thickly

1 onion, diced finely

a generous pinch of dried chilli flakes

1 teaspoon ground cumin

1 teaspoon garam masala

75 g (2¾ oz) frozen peas

1 egg, beaten

1 Preheat the oven to Gas Mark 6/200°C/fan oven 180°C and spray a 1.2 litre (2 pint) ovenproof dish with the cooking spray. Put the potatoes in a large pan and cover with cold water. Bring to the boil, add the parsnips and cook for 7 minutes. Add the cabbage and cook for a further 3 minutes.

2 Meanwhile, heat a non stick frying pan until hot and spray with the cooking spray. Cook the onion for 3–4 minutes until beginning to soften. Add the chilli flakes, cumin and garam masala. Cook for 30 seconds.

3 Drain the potatoes, parsnips and cabbage and return to the pan. Roughly mash everything together, keeping it chunky. Stir in the onion and spices, peas and beaten egg until combined. Spoon into the ovenproof dish, pressing down with the back of a spoon. Spray with the cooking spray and bake in the oven for 30–35 minutes until golden.

Serving suggestion Serve with a diced cucumber, tomato, onion and fresh mint salad, for no extra **POINTS** values.

minestrone salad

All the flavours of the traditional soup but in a salad. Deliciously different.

Serves 2

Takes 15 minutes

4 POINTS values per recipe

152 calories per serving

goes well with...

The Blackberry and Apple Delight on page 188, for an extra 2 POINTS values per serving.

75 g (2¾ oz) dried wholewheat spaghetti, broken into short lengths

60 g (2 oz) fine green beans, trimmed and halved

30 g (1¼ oz) frozen peas

2 baby courgettes, sliced

½ fennel bulb, trimmed and sliced finely

½ teaspoon vegetable gravy granules

1 teaspoon Dijon mustard

75 g (2¾ oz) red or yellow cherry tomatoes, trimmed and halved

a generous handful of fresh basil leaves

a generous handful of parsley leaves

salt and freshly ground black pepper

1 Bring a large pan of water to the boil. Cook the spaghetti for 5–6 minutes, then add the beans, peas, courgettes and fennel. Cook for 2–3 minutes until just tender. Drain, reserving a ladleful of cooking liquid, about 50 ml (2 fl oz). Rinse the spaghetti and vegetables in cold water until cold. Drain again thoroughly and put into a salad bowl.

2 Mix the gravy granules and mustard into the hot reserved cooking liquid until slightly thickened. Add this and the tomatoes, basil and parsley leaves to the salad bowl. Toss to combine. Check the seasoning and serve immediately.

Variation You can add 100 g (3½ oz) torn, wafer thin ham to the salad bowl, for 3 **POINTS** values per serving.

filling and fabulous

chargrilled vegetable tabbouleh

*Baby vegetables are a great addition to this salad, but if you can't find them then use regular size aubergine, leeks and courgettes and cut them into small pieces. The **POINTS** values will remain the same.*

 Serves 2

Takes *35 minutes*

4½ POINTS *values per recipe*

189 calories *per serving*

60 g (2 oz) dried bulgur wheat

300 ml (10 fl oz) vegetable stock

1 red pepper, de-seeded and cut into pieces

3 baby courgettes, halved lengthways

2 baby leeks, halved lengthways

3 baby aubergines, trimmed and halved

low fat cooking spray

juice of a lemon

1 tablespoon finely chopped fresh mint

1 tablespoon finely chopped fresh coriander

1 tablespoon finely chopped fresh flat leaf parsley

4 tablespoons 0% fat Greek yogurt

salt and freshly ground black pepper

1 Put the bulgur wheat and vegetable stock into a saucepan and bring to the boil. Simmer for 10–15 minutes until tender.

2 Meanwhile, heat a griddle pan or non stick frying pan until hot and spray the pepper, courgettes, leeks, and aubergine with the cooking spray. In batches, cook the vegetables in the pan for 8–10 minutes, until charred and cooked. Transfer each batch to a large salad bowl and cover with clingfilm.

3 Drain the bulgur wheat and stir it into the cooked vegetables. Squeeze over the lemon juice and toss through the herbs and season. Serve immediately, topped with 2 tablespoons of the Greek yogurt each.

baked couscous with tomatoes

*This one pot cooking really saves on the washing up. Delicious with a mixed green salad tossed with a fat free dressing, for no additional **POINTS** values.*

 Serves 4

Takes *10 minutes to prepare, 40 minutes to cook*

10½ POINTS *values per recipe*

167 calories *per serving*

6 large tomatoes, halved

2 garlic cloves, sliced

1 tablespoon fresh thyme leaves

2 red or green peppers, de-seeded and cut into large pieces

½ red onion, sliced finely

low fat cooking spray

125 g (4½ oz) dried couscous

300 ml (10 fl oz) vegetable stock

150 g (5½ oz) low fat soft cheese

salt and freshly ground black pepper

1 Preheat the oven to Gas Mark 6/200°C/fan oven 180°C. Arrange the tomatoes, cut side up, in a deep roasting tin. Top with the garlic and thyme. Scatter around the peppers and onion and spray with the cooking spray. Bake for 20 minutes.

2 Carefully remove the tomatoes and set aside. Add the couscous to the roasting tin and pour in the vegetable stock. Carefully return the tomatoes, cut side up and continue to bake in the oven for 10 minutes.

3 Dot the soft cheese over the tomatoes and couscous. Cook for a further 5–10 minutes until the couscous is tender and the stock has been absorbed. Season generously and serve immediately.

aubergine bake

3 POINTS VALUE

ⓨ Serves 2

Takes *15 minutes to prepare,*
40 minutes to cook

6 POINTS *values per recipe*

203 calories *per serving*

goes well with...

**The Crispy Green Medley
on page 169, for an
extra 1 POINTS value per
serving.**

low fat cooking spray

1 onion, chopped finely

1 garlic clove, crushed

1 tablespoon tomato purée

1 x 400 g can chopped tomatoes

½ x 25 g pack fresh basil, torn

**1 large aubergine, trimmed and
sliced thinly lengthways**

**75 g (2¾ oz) taleggio, cut into
small pieces**

1 Preheat the oven to Gas Mark 5/190°C/fan oven 170°C. Heat a non stick saucepan until hot and spray with the cooking spray. Cook the onion for 3–4 minutes until starting to soften and then add the garlic and tomato purée. Cook for 1 minute. Stir in the tomatoes and basil and remove from the heat. Set aside.

2 Heat a griddle pan or non stick frying pan until hot and spray the aubergine slices with the cooking spray. Cook the aubergine slices for 5 minutes, in batches until charred. Pour one third of the tomato sauce in the bottom of a 850 ml (1½ pint) ovenproof dish and top with half the aubergine slices.

3 Dot half the taleggio on top of the aubergine slices and pour over half of the remaining tomato sauce. Top with the remaining aubergine slices, tomato sauce and finish with the taleggio. Bake in the oven for 40 minutes until golden and bubbling. Serve immediately.

crunchy courgette fritters

To get ahead, make these in the morning and chill in the fridge at the end of step 2.

 Serves 4

Takes *30 minutes + 15 minutes cooling, 20 minutes to cook*

14 POINTS *values per recipe*

240 calories *per serving*

low fat cooking spray

1 onion, diced finely

1 courgette, trimmed and grated coarsely

100 g (3½ oz) dried brown rice

2 eggs, beaten

zest of ½ a lemon

8 fresh basil leaves, torn finely

5 x 15 g (½ oz) wholewheat crispbreads

60 g (2 oz) low fat soft cheese

salt and freshly ground black pepper

1 Cook the rice in boiling water for 25 minutes until tender or according to the pack instructions. Drain thoroughly. Preheat the oven to Gas Mark 7/220°C/fan oven 200°C.

2 Meanwhile, heat a wide non stick pan and spray with the cooking spray. Cook the onion for 3–4 minutes until softened. Add the courgette and cooked rice and cook for 5 minutes until sticky. Remove from the heat and stir in the beaten eggs, lemon zest and basil. Season and leave to cool for 15 minutes.

3 Meanwhile, whizz the crispbreads in a food processor, or with a hand blender, until fine crumbs. Mix into the rice mixture along with the soft cheese. Using your hands, shape the mixture into 12 small patties and put on to a non stick baking tray.

4 Spray the courgette fritters with the cooking spray and bake in the oven for 15–20 minutes, turning halfway until golden. Serve immediately.

Serving suggestion Enjoy with a baby leaf salad and 60 g (2 oz) broad beans per person, mixed with diced tomato and onion, for an extra ½ **POINTS** value per serving.

spicy spinach cannelloni

Turn up the heat with this classic dish by adding piquante cayenne pepper. If you prefer less heat, use mild chilli powder instead. The **POINTS** values will remain the same.

Ⓥ **Serves 4**

Takes *15 minutes to prepare, 40 minutes to cook*

14½ POINTS *values per recipe*

267 calories *per serving*

1 x 400 g can chopped tomatoes with onion and herbs

100 ml (3½ fl oz) vegetable stock

1 x 250 g pot Quark

1 egg yolk

1 red chilli, de-seeded and chopped finely

375 g (13 oz) frozen spinach, defrosted

150 g (5½ oz) low fat soft cheese with garlic and herbs

½ teaspoon cayenne pepper

125 g (4½ oz) cannelloni tubes (about 12)

2 tablespoons fresh, roughly chopped coriander, to serve

1 Preheat the oven to Gas Mark 6/200°C/fan oven 180°C. In a jug, mix together the tomatoes and vegetable stock. Set aside. In a bowl, mix together the Quark, egg yolk and chilli. Set aside.

2 Squeeze out the excess water from the spinach and put into a large bowl. Mix with the soft cheese and cayenne pepper. Using a piping bag and a 2 cm (¾ inch) nozzle, pipe the mixture into the cannelloni tubes and arrange in an 1.75 litre (3 pint) ovenproof dish. Pour over the tomato sauce.

3 Dollop the Quark mixture over the top. With the back of a spoon, spread the mixture to join up the dollops. It doesn't matter if the tomato sauce marbles a little with the Quark. Bake in the oven for 35–40 minutes until golden and the pasta is cooked. Scatter over the coriander and serve immediately.

Tip If you don't have a piping bag, use a teaspoon to stuff the cannelloni - it will just take a little bit longer.

3½ POINTS VALUE

mushroom pilaff

If you can't find exotic frozen mushrooms then use a selection of fresh ones such as porcini, oyster and chestnut mushrooms.

Ⓥ Serves 4

Takes *10 minutes to prepare + 10 minutes standing, 25 minutes to cook*

14 POINTS *values per recipe*

256 calories *per serving*

low fat cooking spray

1 x 300 g pack frozen exotic mushrooms

1 red onion, **sliced finely**

1 tablespoon finely chopped fresh sage

250 g (9 oz) dried brown basmati rice

300 ml (10 fl oz) hot vegetable stock

4 tablespoons 0% fat Greek yogurt

½ teaspoon paprika

1 Heat a deep, wide, lidded non stick pan and spray with the cooking spray. Cook the frozen mushrooms for 5 minutes, then add the onion and sage and cook for 3–4 minutes until starting to brown.

2 Stir in the rice and vegetable stock, cover tightly and cook for 20–25 minutes until the rice is tender. Take off the heat and leave to stand covered for 10 minutes. (Do not lift the lid.)

3 Divide between four warmed plates, each topped with 1 tablespoon of yogurt and a sprinkling of paprika.

Serving suggestion Serve with a baby spinach salad drizzled with a fat free dressing, for no extra **POINTS** values per serving.

deliciously different

ratatouille pie

4 POINTS VALUE

Ratatouille, the classic Provençal vegetable stew, makes a great filling for this pie. Serve with a mixture of cooked beans, such as **runner beans,** *for no additional* **POINTS** *values.*

Ⓥ Serves 4
Takes *30 minutes to prepare,*
40 minutes to cook
16 POINTS *values per recipe*
262 calories *per serving*

1 tablespoon cornflour
low fat cooking spray
2 courgettes, cut into chunks
1 red pepper, de-seeded and cut
    into chunks
1 red onion, chopped roughly
1 large aubergine, cut into chunks

4 tomatoes, quartered
1 garlic clove, crushed
1 tablespoon fresh thyme leaves
2 tablespoons sun dried tomato
    paste
150 g (5½ oz) ready rolled puff
    pastry, from a 375 g pack

1 Preheat the oven to Gas Mark 5/190°C/fan oven 170°C. Dissolve the cornflour in 2 tablespoons of cold water and set aside. Heat a wide, lidded non stick pan and spray with the cooking spray. Cook the courgettes, pepper, onion and aubergine for 10 minutes, stirring occasionally until starting to brown.

2 Add the tomatoes and garlic, cover and cook gently for 10 minutes, stirring occasionally to mash up some of the tomatoes. Stir in the cornflour mixture, thyme and tomato paste and cook for 1 minute. Take off the heat and spoon into a 1.2 litre (2 pint) ovenproof dish and level the top. Leave to cool slightly.

3 Unroll and then cut the pastry into four squares and then each square in half diagonally to make eight triangles. Arrange the triangles down the centre of the dish with the points all facing the same way, overlapping each triangle slightly. Bake in the oven for 30–40 minutes until golden and bubbling.

spinach gnocchi gratin

A dish that even meat-lovers will enjoy.

Ⓥ Serves 4
Takes *10 minutes to prepare,*
20 minutes to cook
19 POINTS *values per recipe*
343 calories *per serving*

1 x 500 g pack fresh gnocchi
150 g (5½ oz) frozen chopped spinach, defrosted
2 garlic cloves, crushed
1 x 250 g pot reduced fat onion and chive cottage cheese
2 egg yolks
50 g (1¾ oz) mild or hot pepperdew peppers, sliced finely
15 g (½ oz) pine nut kernels, toasted
freshly ground black pepper

1 Preheat the oven to Gas Mark 4/180°C/fan oven 160°C. Bring a large pan of water to the boil, add the gnocchi and cook for 2 minutes. Drain and return to the pan.
2 Meanwhile, squeeze the excess water from the spinach and put into a large bowl. Stir in the garlic, cottage cheese, egg yolks and peppers and lots of freshly ground black pepper. Stir into the gnocchi to coat and then spoon into a 1.2 litre (2 pint) ovenproof dish.
3 Sprinkle over the pine nut kernels and bake in the oven for 20 minutes until golden.

Serving suggestion Serve with a 35 g slice of garlic bread per person and a large, zero **POINTS** value green salad, for an extra 2½ **POINTS** values per serving.

4½ POINTS VALUE

cottage pie

Whisky is the secret ingredient which really jazzes up this midweek classic.

Serves 4

Takes *35 minutes to prepare, 40 minutes to cook*

17½ POINTS *values per recipe*

267 calories *per serving*

250 g (9 oz) swede, **peeled and cut into even chunks**

300 g (10½ oz) potatoes, **peeled and cut into even chunks**

low fat cooking spray

1 small leek, **sliced and rinsed**

1 garlic clove, **crushed**

2 carrots, **peeled and diced finely**

1 celery stick, **diced finely**

2 tablespoons tomato purée

50 ml (2 fl oz) whisky

1 x 350 g pack vegetarian mince e.g. Quorn mince

200 ml (7 fl oz) vegetable stock

50 g (1¾ oz) reduced fat mature Cheddar cheese, grated

salt and freshly ground black pepper

1 Preheat the oven to Gas Mark 4/180°C/fan oven 160°C. Put the swede and potato chunks into a large pan and cover with water. Bring to the boil and simmer for 20 minutes until tender. Drain and mash until smooth. Season generously.

2 Meanwhile, heat a non stick frying pan until hot and spray with the cooking spray. Cook the leek for 5 minutes until softened. Remove and set aside. Spray the pan again and cook the garlic, carrots and celery for 5–8 minutes until softened. Stir in the tomato purée and whisky and cook for 1 minute. Stir in the mince and stock and then spoon it all into a 1.2 litre (2 pint) ovenproof dish.

3 Mix the cooked leek into the mash and then spread the mash over the top of the mince. It's best to put small dollops of mash all over the top and then gently spread the dollops together to cover the mince. Sprinkle over the cheese and bake in the oven for 30–40 minutes until golden and bubbling. Serve immediately.

Serving suggestion Serve with a medium portion of mixed frozen vegetables, for an extra ½ **POINTS** value per serving.

Variation You can use 400 g (14 oz) lean lamb mince, instead of vegetarian mince and brown it in the pan with the carrots and celery in step 2, for 7 **POINTS** values per serving.

b'stilla roll

*This adaptation of the Moroccan b'stilla pie, traditionally made with pigeon and sugared almonds, is great hot or cold. Serve with a generous mixed salad, gherkins and pickled onions, for no extra **POINTS** values.*

Ⓥ Serves 4

Takes *20 minutes to prepare + 10 minutes cooling, 45 minutes to cook*
19 POINTS *values per recipe*
311 calories *per serving*

4 eggs
½ x 25 g pack fresh flat leaf parsley, chopped roughly
½ x 25 g pack fresh coriander, chopped roughly
1 preserved lemon from a jar, drained, pips removed and diced finely
1 x 350 g pack Quorn Chicken Style Pieces
a generous pinch of saffron
1 tablespoon cornflour
8 x 15 g sheets filo pastry
low fat cooking spray
15 g (½ oz) flaked almonds
freshly ground black pepper

1 Preheat the oven to Gas Mark 4/180°C/fan oven 160°C. Put 3 eggs into a small saucepan and cover with water. Bring to the boil and simmer for 8 minutes. Drain and plunge into cold water.

2 Meanwhile, in a large bowl, mix together the parsley, coriander, diced lemon, Quorn pieces, saffron and freshly ground black pepper. Dissolve the cornflour in 2 tablespoons of cold water to make a paste. Peel the eggs and chop roughly. Stir into the Quorn mixture with the cornflour paste.

3 Lay a sheet of filo pastry on a non stick baking tray and spray with the cooking spray. Take another filo sheet and lay it next to the other filo sheet, overlapping one long edge slightly to make a rectangle measuring 30 cm x 25 cm (12 inches x 10 inches). Spray again and repeat the layering until all the sheets are used.

4 Spread the Quorn mixture over the rectangle leaving a 2½ cm (1 inch) border all the way around. Spray the exposed filo pastry with the cooking spray and fold over the pastry of the two short sides. Roll up the pastry starting from one long side like a big Swiss roll.

5 Beat the remaining egg and brush over the pastry. Sprinkle with the almonds and bake in the oven for 40–45 minutes until golden.

6 Leave to cool for 10 minutes, then cut into four and serve immediately.

Variation You can replace the Quorn pieces with 350 g (12 oz) cooked shredded skinless chicken, for 5½ **POINTS** values per serving.

red wine mushrooms with polenta mash

Mushrooms are a great alternative to meat due to their dense texture and flavoursome punch.

Ⓥ Serves 2

Takes *15 minutes*

11½ POINTS *values per recipe*

413 calories *per serving*

600 ml (1 pint) vegetable stock

1 teaspoon cornflour

low fat cooking spray

3 shallots, sliced finely

1 garlic clove, crushed

250 g (9 oz) chestnut and oyster mushrooms, wiped and sliced thickly

125 ml (4 fl oz) red wine

2 tablespoons cranberry sauce

1 tablespoon fresh thyme leaves

100 g (3½ oz) quick cook dried polenta

1–2 teaspoons Dijon mustard, to taste

30 g (1¼ oz) vegetarian Parmesan cheese, grated

salt and freshly ground black pepper

1 Pour 400 ml (14 fl oz) of the vegetable stock into a large pan and bring to the boil. Dissolve the cornflour in the remaining stock. Meanwhile, heat a deep, non stick frying pan and spray with the cooking spray. Cook the shallots, garlic and mushrooms for 5 minutes until just starting to brown.

2 Add the red wine to the mushrooms and bubble for a minute until almost evaporated. Stir in the cornflour mixture, cranberry sauce and thyme. Gently heat for 1–2 minutes until thickened. Check the seasoning and keep warm.

3 Once the pan of stock is boiling, add the polenta and cook for 1–2 minutes, stirring until thickened. Be careful, as it will bubble like a volcano. Stir in the mustard and Parmesan cheese. Season and serve immediately with the mushrooms and red wine sauce.

Serving suggestion Serve with cooked broccoli, green beans and 1 tablespoon of peas per person, for an extra ½ **POINTS** value per serving.

Variation If you want to add meat, use only 100 g (3½ oz) mushrooms and then add 175 g (6 oz) sliced, lean fillet steak when cooking the mushrooms, for a **POINTS** value of 8.

chilli tofu noodles

7 POINTS VALUE

Serves 2
Takes *15 minutes*
13½ POINTS *values per recipe*
450 calories *per serving*

low fat cooking spray
150 g (5½ oz) tofu, cubed
25 g (1 oz) fresh ginger, peeled and shredded
1 tablespoon soy sauce
2 tablespoons sweet chilli sauce
30 g (1¼ oz) creamed coconut, chopped finely
juice of a lime
1 x 400 g pack fresh, mixed stir fry vegetables
1 x 150 g pack straight to wok thick udon noodles

1 Heat a wok or non stick frying pan until hot and spray with the cooking spray. Cook the tofu and ginger for 2–3 minutes until starting to brown. Add the soy sauce and bubble for 30 seconds until almost evaporated. Remove the tofu and ginger and set aside.

2 In a bowl, mix together the chilli sauce, creamed coconut and lime juice. Set aside. Heat the wok or pan again and spray with the cooking spray.

3 Stir fry the vegetables and noodles for 4–5 minutes, stirring occasionally and then pour in the chilli mixture and return the tofu. Remove from the heat and keep stirring constantly until coated and the coconut purée has melted. Serve immediately.

Why not **jazz up your meals** with some fantastic 'fill you up' side dishes which will help to stretch your **POINTS** allowance? With these recipes, you can transform the simplest of vegetable dishes such as Bacon and Onion Mash and Breaded Garlic Mushrooms into great tasting dishes. With a selection of accompaniments such as Roasted Nutty Chicory and Citrus Slaw, not to mention Wasabi, Lime and Mayo Dressing and Wild Rocket and Spinach Pesto, you'll be spoilt for choice when you're looking to 'bulk up' your meals. There's **something for every season** here - ideas range from summery Crispy Green Medley to wintery Roasted Root Vegetables. Side orders have never been so exciting.

Crispy Green Medley, *page 169*

stir fried greens

Liven up veggies by cooking them quickly in a hot wok, which retains their goodness and crunch. This recipe can easily be doubled.

Serves 2
Takes 15 minutes
½ **POINTS** values per recipe
65 calories per serving

goes well with...
The Spiced Chicken Parcels on page 54, for an extra 4½ POINTS values per serving.

100 g (3½ oz) **tenderstem** broccoli
low fat cooking spray
100 g (3½ oz) **chopped** curly kale leaf
75 g (2¾ oz) mange tout
½ **teaspoon caraway seeds, crushed lightly**
a generous pinch of dried chilli flakes
1 **tablespoon dark soy sauce**
1 **teaspoon sesame seeds**

1 Cut the florets off the long stalks of the broccoli and set aside. Cut the stalks in half lengthways and then into 2½ cm (1 inch) pieces. Heat a wok or non stick frying pan until really hot and spray with the cooking spray. Cook the broccoli stalks and curly kale for 3 minutes, stirring occasionally.
2 Add the broccoli florets and mange tout to the pan and cook for 2 minutes. Stir in the caraway seeds and chilli flakes and continue to stir fry for 2–4 minutes, stirring occasionally. Remove from the heat, add the soy sauce and scatter over the sesame seeds. Serve immediately.

wild rocket and spinach pesto

This peppery sauce is great for stirring through cooked pasta, spooning on to a griddle steak or swirling into soup. It will last for up to 3 days in the fridge.

Serves 4
Takes 5 minutes
1½ **POINTS** values per recipe
21 calories per serving

goes well with...
The Chilled Tomato Soup on page 28, for no extra POINTS values.

1 x 25 g **pack fresh** basil, **leaves only**
½ x 120 g **bag** watercress, spinach and rocket salad
2 garlic cloves, **chopped roughly**
60 g (2 oz) low fat soft cheese
2 **tablespoons cold vegetable stock**
salt and freshly ground black pepper

1 Put the basil, watercress, spinach and rocket salad and garlic in a food processor, or blender, and blend until finely minced.
2 Add the soft cheese and replace the lid, while blending continuously. Pour in the vegetable stock until it is fully mixed without separating. Season and use when needed.

satisfying greens

citrus slaw

This fruity coleslaw is perfect with barbecued food.

Ⓨ Serves 6
Takes *10 minutes*
2½ POINTS *values per recipe*
62 calories *per serving*

goes well with...

The Chicken Cordon Bleu on page 88, for an extra 3½ POINTS values per serving.

- 1 **fennel bulb**, trimmed, quartered and shredded finely
- 1 **red onion**, sliced finely
- ½ **white cabbage**, tough outer leaves removed, cored and shredded finely
- 1 x 200 g pot **fat free mandarin yogurt**
- 1 tablespoon **wholegrain mustard**
- 1 large **orange**
- 1 x 25 g pack fresh **flat leaf parsley**, chopped roughly
- 1 teaspoon **dried pomegranate seeds**, crushed lightly
- **salt and freshly ground black pepper**

1 Put the fennel, onion and cabbage into a large salad bowl. Add the yogurt and mustard. Season and stir through until coated.
2 Cut the top and base off the orange and stand upright on a board. Using a serrated knife, carefully cut away the peel and pith. Remove the segments by cutting between the membranes. (Do this over the salad bowl to catch the juices).
3 Cut each orange segment in half and then gently fold into the salad bowl, along with the parsley and pomegranate seeds. Check the seasoning and serve immediately.

Serving suggestion Use as a topping for a 225 g (8 oz) **jacket potato** per person, for an extra 2½ **POINTS** values per serving.

crispy green medley

Crunchy vegetables with piquant onions and peppers make the perfect side dish.

Ⓨ Serves 4
Takes *5 minutes*
4½ POINTS *values per recipe*
110 calories *per serving*

goes well with...

The Aubergine Bake on page 152, for an extra 3 POINTS values per serving.

- 100 g (3½ oz) **asparagus spears**, trimmed and cut into short lengths
- 60 g (2 oz) **mange tout**
- 100 g (3½ oz) **sugar snap peas**
- 75 g (2¾ oz) small **pickled onions**, drained and sliced
- 1 x 410 g can **chick peas** in water, drained and rinsed
- ½ x 85 g bag **wild rocket**
- 50 g (1¾ oz) mild or hot **pepperdew peppers**, drained and sliced finely
- 3 tablespoons **fat free Italian style dressing**
- **salt and freshly ground black pepper**

1 Bring a large pan of water to the boil and plunge in the asparagus, mange tout and sugar snap peas. Bring back to the boil and cook for 1 minute. Drain and rinse in cold water until cold. Drain again thoroughly.
2 Transfer to a large salad bowl and toss with the onions, chick peas, rocket, peppers and Italian style dressing. Check the seasoning and serve immediately.

carrot and courgette spiced salad

If making the salad in advance, keep the dressing separate and then stir through when needed.

Ⓨ Serves 4
Takes *15 minutes*
3½ POINTS *values per recipe*
81 calories *per serving*

goes well with...

The Nutty Lamb Kebabs on page 75, for an additional 4½ POINTS values per serving.

grated zest and juice of ½ an orange
2 shallots, sliced finely
½ teaspoon ground ginger
½ teaspoon cumin seeds, crushed lightly
2 teaspoons sherry vinegar
1 tablespoon extra virgin olive oil
1 large courgette, trimmed
2 large carrots, peeled
2 teaspoons sesame seeds, toasted
½ x 25 g pack fresh mint, leaves only
2 tablespoons roughly chopped fresh coriander
salt and freshly ground black pepper

1 In a jug, whisk together the orange zest and juice, shallots, ginger, cumin seeds, sherry vinegar and olive oil. Season and set aside. Meanwhile, using a potato peeler, starting on one side cut the courgette into ribbons, stopping when you get to the seeds. Then start on the other side and continue until all that is left is a column of seeds. Discard the seeds. Transfer the courgette ribbons to a large salad bowl.

2 Using the potato peeler again, cut the carrot into thin ribbons. Put the ribbons into the bowl and toss with the dressing, half the sesame seeds and mint and coriander leaves. Sprinkle over the remaining sesame seeds and serve.

wasabi, lime and mayo dressing

Be warned, wasabi can be very hot.

Ⓥ Serves 6
Takes *5 minutes*
8½ POINTS *values per recipe*
60 calories *per serving*

goes well with...
The Crunchy Parmesan Chicken on page 43, for an extra 5 POINTS values per serving.

100 g (3½ oz) reduced fat mayonnaise
100 g (3½ oz) low fat plain yogurt
2 teaspoons wasabi paste
zest and juice of 2 limes

1 tablespoon finely chopped fresh coriander
salt and freshly ground black pepper

1 Mix all the ingredients together in a bowl and season.

Variations *Chilli and coriander* Replace the wasabi paste with 50 g (1¾ oz) sweet chilli sauce, for the same **POINTS** values.
Dill and caper Replace the wasabi paste, lime and coriander with 15 g (½ oz) capers in sherry vinegar, drained and chopped, the zest and juice of a lemon and 1 tablespoon finely chopped fresh dill, for the same **POINTS** values.

red wine gravy

This basic recipe for gravy is great to have to hand, for any gravy moment.

Serves 4
Takes *30 minutes*
5 POINTS *values per recipe*
100 calories *per serving*

goes well with...
The Greek Roast Lamb on page 77, for an extra 5 POINTS values per serving.

low fat cooking spray
1 onion, chopped roughly
1 carrot, peeled and chopped
1 celery stick, chopped
1 dried bouquet garni
200 ml (7 fl oz) red wine
600 ml (1 pint) beef stock

1 tablespoon plain flour
2 teaspoons low fat polyunsaturated margarine
1 tablespoon redcurrant jelly
salt and freshly ground black pepper

1 Heat a wide, lidded pan. Spray with cooking spray. Gently cook the onion, carrot, celery and bouquet garni. Cover for 5–8 minutes until softened.

2 Add the red wine, bring to the boil and bubble rapidly for 3 minutes until reduced by two thirds. Pour in the beef stock and bring back to the boil. Gently simmer for 10 minutes until reduced by a third. Meanwhile, whisk together the flour, margarine and redcurrant jelly until smooth.

3 Pour the red wine mixture through a sieve over a clean pan, gently pushing through all the liquid. Discard the vegetables and sediment. Bring the red wine mixture to the boil, whisk in the flour mixture, constantly whisking until smooth. Bubble for a minute until thickened, check the seasoning and serve immediately.

Variations *Mushroom gravy* In step 2, after adding the redcurrant jelly, stir in 100 g (3½ oz) sliced mushrooms, gently cooked in low fat cooking spray for 5 minutes until softened, for the same **POINTS** values.
Onion gravy In step 2, after adding the redcurrant jelly, stir in 1 sliced red onion, gently cooked in low fat cooking spray for 10-15 minutes until softened and caramelised, for the same **POINTS** values.

roasted root vegetables

(1½ POINTS VALUE)

These are so versatile and make a tasty change to roast potatoes.

Ⓥ **Serves 4**

Takes *15 minutes to prepare,* 1¼ *hours to cook*

5 POINTS *values per recipe*

125 calories *per serving*

goes well with...

The Pot Roast on page 117, for an extra 4 POINTS values per serving.

3 **parsnips, peeled**

200 g (7 oz) **new** potatoes

225 g (8 oz) **butternut squash,** **peeled and de-seeded**

2 **carrots, peeled**

1 **red onion, chopped roughly**

4 **garlic cloves, unpeeled**

4 **sprigs of fresh** thyme

2 **sprigs of fresh** rosemary

low fat cooking spray

1 **tablespoon sherry vinegar**

salt and freshly ground black **pepper**

1 Preheat the oven to Gas Mark 6/200°C/fan oven 180°C. Cut the parsnips, potatoes, squash and carrots into even sized chunks. Put everything into a large roasting tray along with the red onion, garlic, thyme and rosemary.

2 Spray with the cooking spray and toss to coat. Cover with foil and bake in the oven for 30 minutes. Remove the foil and cook for a further 45 minutes until roasted and caramelised.

3 Stir through the sherry vinegar, season and serve immediately.

breaded garlic mushrooms

Spoil the whole family with this great classic. Mushrooms can be prepared up to the end of step 2 and then chilled in the fridge for up to 1 day.

Y **Serves 4**
Takes *10 minutes to prepare, 20 minutes to cook*
7½ POINTS *values per recipe*
170 calories *per serving*

goes well with...

The Mushroom Spiced Steak on page 68, for an extra 3½ POINTS values per serving.

15 g (½ oz) **plain flour**
150 g (5½ oz) **small** chestnut mushrooms, **wiped and trimmed**
150 g (5½ oz) **baby** portabello mushrooms, **wiped and trimmed**
2 teaspoons **garlic purée**
2 eggs, **beaten**
100 g (3½ oz) **fresh breadcrumbs**
low fat cooking spray
1 teaspoon **paprika**

1 Preheat the oven to Gas Mark 6/200°C/fan oven 180°C. Put the flour into a large bowl, add the mushrooms and toss until coated. It is best to use your hands. Mix together the garlic purée and eggs and put into another large bowl. Empty the floured mushrooms into the garlic and egg mixture and toss until coated. Again, it is best to use your hands.

2 Put the breadcrumbs into the empty flour bowl and drain away any egg from the mushrooms. Empty the mushrooms into the breadcrumbs and gently toss until coated.

3 Transfer to a non stick baking tray. Spray with the cooking spray and bake in the oven for 20 minutes, turning halfway through until golden and crispy. Sprinkle with the paprika and serve immediately.

make a good dinner great

roasted nutty chicory

Chicory is a bitter leaf found next to the lettuce in most large supermarkets. Choose one with yellow or red leaf tips not green ones, otherwise it will be too bitter.

ⓨ **Serves 4**

Takes *5 minutes to prepare, 25 minutes to cook*

8½ POINTS values per recipe

126 calories per serving

goes well with...

The Beef Wellington Pie on page 99, for an extra 6 POINTS values per serving.

1 red onion, sliced finely

low fat cooking spray

6 chicory bulbs, trimmed and halved.

50 g (1¾ oz) Stilton, crumbled

25 g (1 oz) walnut halves, chopped roughly

2 teaspoons sherry vinegar

freshly ground black pepper

1 Preheat the oven to Gas Mark 5/190°C/fan oven 170°C. Put the sliced onion on a non stick roasting tray and spray with the cooking spray. Bake in the oven for 10 minutes.

2 Remove the roasting tray from the oven and transfer the onions to a bowl or plate. Put the chicory halves cut side up on the baking tray. Sprinkle the cooked onion over the top, along with the Stilton and walnut halves.

3 Spray again with the cooking spray and bake in the oven for 10–15 minutes until melted and golden. Drizzle over the sherry vinegar, season with freshly ground black pepper and serve immediately.

creamy potato salad

Great for packed lunches or barbecues or to liven up a piece of chicken or fish.

ⓨ **Serves 4**

Takes *10 minutes to prepare + cooling, 15 minutes to cook*

7½ POINTS values per recipe

120 calories per serving

goes well with...

The Spiced Cod Kebabs on page 126, for an extra 1½ POINTS values per serving.

500 g (1 lb 2 oz) waxy new potatoes, such as Charlotte, peeled

2 tablespoons white balsamic vinegar

zest of a lemon

1 red chilli, de-seeded and diced finely

1 x 25 g pack fresh coriander, chopped roughly

1 x 25 g pack fresh parsley, chopped roughly

100 g (3½ oz) frozen peas, defrosted

2 tablespoons 0% fat Greek yogurt

salt and freshly ground black pepper

1 Cut the potatoes into fairly thick slices. Put the potatoes into a large saucepan and cover with cold water. Bring to the boil and simmer for 10–15 minutes until just tender. Drain and return to the pan. Stir in the balsamic vinegar, lemon zest and chilli. Season and leave to cool slightly.

2 Put the coriander, parsley and peas in a large salad bowl. Add the cool potatoes and yogurt and toss gently. Check the seasoning and serve.

spring onion and Cheddar tray bread

The aroma of home baked bread is simply irresistible.

 ❄ **Serves 12**

Takes *25 minutes to prepare + 1½ hours proving, 20 minutes to bake*

28 POINTS *values per recipe*

157 calories *per serving*

goes well with...

The Herbed Goat's Cheese Pâté on page 37, for an extra 3½ POINTS values per serving.

500 g (1 lb 2 oz) strong white bread flour, plus 1 tablespoon for dusting

1 x 7 g sachet fast action dried yeast

1 teaspoon caster sugar

2 teaspoons mustard powder

50 g (1¾ oz) reduced fat Cheddar cheese, diced finely

4 spring onions, trimmed and sliced finely

low fat cooking spray

1 Mix the flour, yeast, sugar and mustard powder in a bowl and make a well in the centre of the mixture. Pour in 350 ml (12 fl oz) warm water and mix together to a smooth dough. Add a splash more water if there are any dry bits.

2 Dust the surface with 1 tablespoon of flour and empty the dough on to the surface. Knead for 5 minutes until smooth and elastic. Roll lightly until flat and scatter over three quarters of the cheese and spring onions. Roll up the dough like a Swiss roll and then lightly roll it out again to about 28 cm x 18 cm (11 inches x 7 inches).

3 Spray a 30 cm x 20 cm (12 inches x 8 inches) baking tray with the cooking spray and put the dough into the tray. Scatter over the remaining cheese and spring onions. Spray a piece of clingfilm with the cooking spray and use to cover the tray, sprayed side down. Leave it in a warm place for 1–1½ hours or until it has doubled in size.

4 Preheat the oven to Gas Mark 7/220°C/200°C fan oven. Remove the clingfilm from the tray and discard. Score the bread into 12 pieces and then bake in the oven for 20 minutes until golden and the base sounds hollow when tapped. Cool on a wire rack before serving.

bacon and onion mash

This is the ultimate way with spuds and just the thing for mopping up delicious juices.

Serves 4
Takes *35 minutes*
12 *POINTS values per recipe*
155 calories *per serving*

goes well with...

The Herby Chicken Casserole on page 115, for an extra 4 POINTS values per serving.

600 g (1 lb 5 oz) floury potatoes, **peeled and cut into even chunks**
1 large garlic clove
low fat cooking spray
1 onion, **sliced finely**
2 rashers smoked lean back bacon
3 tablespoons low fat fromage frais
1 tablespoon snipped fresh chives
freshly ground black pepper

1 Preheat the grill to medium. Put the potatoes and garlic into a saucepan and cover with cold water. Bring to the boil and simmer for 20 minutes until tender. At the same time, heat a lidded, non stick pan and spray with the cooking spray. On a very low heat, cook the onion, covered, for 15 minutes, stirring occasionally until softened and caramelised.

2 Meanwhile, put the bacon on a grill pan and cook for 5 minutes, turning halfway through until cooked and crispy. Drain on kitchen paper, then chop finely.

3 Drain the potatoes and garlic thoroughly and return to the saucepan. Mash with a potato masher until smooth. Stir in the fromage frais, chives, cooked bacon and onion. Season with plenty of freshly ground black pepper and serve immediately.

Serving suggestion Enjoy with two low fat, thick pork sausages per person and green beans, for an extra 2½ **POINTS** values per serving.

polenta and olive chips

Crispy on the outside and creamy in the middle – chips never tasted so good. These can be prepared up to 1 day in advance, up to the end of step 2.

Ⓥ Serves 2

Takes *20 minutes to prepare + 30 minutes to cool, 25 minutes to cook*

5½ POINTS *values per recipe*

214 calories *per serving*

goes well with...

The Italian Haddock Bake on page 87, for an extra 3 POINTS values per serving.

450 ml (16 fl oz) vegetable stock
100 g (3½ oz) quick cook dried polenta
30 g (1¼ oz) stoned black olives in brine, drained and chopped finely
¼ red pepper, de-seeded and chopped finely
1 tablespoon finely chopped fresh flat leaf parsley
low fat cooking spray
salt and freshly ground pepper

1 Line an 18 cm (7 inch) square baking tin with clingfilm (it helps to first brush the tin with a little cold water). Put the vegetable stock into a large saucepan and bring to the boil.

2 Stir the polenta into the stock, continuously stirring and cook for 1 minute or according to the packet instructions until thick. Remove from the heat and quickly stir in the olives, pepper and parsley. Season. Pour into the prepared baking tin, level it with the back of a spoon, tapping the tin on the work surface until flat, and set aside for 30 minutes.

3 Preheat the oven to Gas Mark 7/220°C/fan oven 200°C. Remove the polenta from the tin and discard the clingfilm. Cut into 16 chunky chips and transfer to a non stick baking tray. Spray with the cooking spray and bake in the oven for 20–25 minutes until golden. Serve immediately.

Parisienne potatoes

Serves 4

Takes *15 minutes to prepare, 45 minutes to cook*

13½ POINTS *values per recipe*

202 calories *per serving*

goes well with...

The Braised Italian Chicken on page 119, for an extra 4½ POINTS values per serving.

low fat cooking spray

550 g (1 lb 4 oz) floury potatoes**, peeled and cut into bite size cubes**

1 onion**, sliced finely**

100 ml (3½ fl oz) vegetable stock

50 ml (2 fl oz) dry white wine

1 x 200 g pack low fat soft cheese

1 garlic clove**, crushed**

3 x 15 g (½ oz) slices Parma ham**, cut in half lengthways**

freshly ground black pepper

1 Preheat the oven to Gas Mark 5/190°C/fan oven 170°C and spray a 1½ litre (2¾ pint) ovenproof dish with the cooking spray. Put the potato and onion into a saucepan and cover with cold water. Bring to the boil and simmer for 3–5 minutes. Drain thoroughly and return to the pan. In a jug, mix together the stock, wine, soft cheese, garlic and freshly ground black pepper.

2 Pour the soft cheese mixture over the potatoes and gently stir to coat. Spoon half the potatoes and onion into the ovenproof dish and season with freshly ground black pepper. Lay half the Parma ham on top and then cover with the remaining potato mixture. Lay the remaining Parma ham on top.

3 Bake in the oven for 45 minutes until golden and the potatoes are tender. Serve immediately.

If you find that a meal isn't completely satisfying unless it ends with something sweet, then be prepared to be **spoiled for choice**. Whether it's rich dark chocolate you're after or juicy fruits, there is definitely something for everyone here. Many are low in **POINTS** values so there's no need to worry about going over your **POINTS** allowance. Try the Chocolate Marshmallow Meringue Cake or Frozen Raspberry Tiramisu. If time is limited and you need an instant pud, then the Vanilla and Passion Fruit Cups or Quick Banana Ice cream are great choices. However, if you need to impress then the Sparkling Fruit Jellies or Orange Panna cotta are really **easy to prepare** and look fantastic. If you fancy an afternoon bake-in, then the Tray Bake Date Scones and Spiced Pear Cake will have the baker in you screaming to come out.

Apricot Surprise Pudding, *page 196*

desserts

slow roasted plums

Cooking at a low temperature for a long time brings out the natural sugars in the plums.

6 slightly under ripe plums, halved and stoned
2 tablespoons balsamic vinegar
2 teaspoons vanilla extract
2 sprigs of fresh lemon thyme, leaves only

Ⓨ **Serves 4**
Takes *10 minutes to prepare, 1½ hours to cook*
1½ POINTS values per recipe
46 calories *per serving*

goes well after...

The Creamy Peppercorn Beef on page 72, for an extra 4½ POINTS values per serving.

1 Preheat the oven to Gas Mark 2/150°C/fan oven 130°C. Put the plum halves into a small ovenproof dish and bake in the oven for 1 hour.

2 Meanwhile, mix together the balsamic vinegar, vanilla, sprigs of thyme and 4 tablespoons of cold water in a bowl. Pour over the plums and continue to cook for 30 minutes until the juices have reduced to a syrup. Enjoy hot or cold.

Serving suggestion Serve with 1 tablespoon of **low fat fromage frais** per person, for an added 1 **POINTS** value per serving.

rhubarb and custard pots

The famous school duo take on a new twist in this creamy pudding.

Ⓨ **Serves 4**

Takes *10 minutes to prepare + 1 hour to chill, 50 minutes to cook*

5½ POINTS *values per recipe*

61 calories *per serving*

goes well after...

The Balsamic Lamb Chops on page 71, for an extra 4½ POINTS values per serving.

225 g (8 oz) rhubarb, trimmed and diced

zest of an orange

1 tablespoon artificial sweetener

3 egg yolks

1 teaspoon vanilla extract

300 ml (10 fl oz) skimmed milk

1 Preheat the oven to Gas Mark 3/160°C/fan oven 140°C. Put the rhubarb in a lidded saucepan with 2 tablespoons of cold water, orange zest and 2 teaspoons of sweetener. Cover and cook for 5 minutes until stewed. Put the rhubarb into a sieve over a bowl and press with the back of a spoon to squeeze out the juice. Reserve both the juice and the fruit.

2 In a jug, mix together the egg yolks, remaining sweetener and vanilla extract until smooth. In a saucepan, gently warm the milk until bubbles appear around the edge of the pan. Gradually pour the milk into the jug, stirring until combined. Pass through another sieve into a jug and mix with the sieved rhubarb fruit.

3 Divide between four 200 ml (7 fl oz) ramekins. Place a piece of kitchen paper in the base of a deep roasting pan and sit the ramekins on top to prevent them from slipping in the tin. Pour cold water into the pan until halfway up the sides of the ramekins and bake for 50 minutes until just set with a slight wobble in the middle.

4 Leave to cool and then chill for at least 1 hour. To serve, flood the tops of the custards with the reserved rhubarb juice.

sugary and sweet

vanilla and passion fruit cups

These simple desserts are refreshingly delicious.

Ⓥ Serves 4
Takes *10 minutes*
6½ POINTS *values per recipe*
114 calories *per serving*

goes well after...
The Olive Crusted Pork on page 74, for an extra 4½ POINTS values per serving.

6 ripe passion fruits
zest of ½ an orange
½ ripe mango (about 150 g/5½ oz), peeled, stoned and diced finely
1 x 250 g pot Quark
2 x 200 g pot virtually fat free vanilla yogurt

1 Cut four passion fruit in half and scoop the pulp out into a sieve over a bowl. Press the pulp through the sieve using the back of a spoon and then discard the seeds. Cut the remaining passion fruit in half and scoop the pulp into the bowl of juice along with the orange zest and diced mango.

2 Divide the mango and passion fruit mixture between four 200 ml (7 fl oz) glass cups or small bowls. Mix together the Quark and yogurt until smooth. Spoon a large dollop of the yogurt mixture into each cup on top of the mango. Serve immediately.

blackberry and apple delight

Tapioca is a pearl like grain that can be found near the pasta and grains in most large supermarkets.

Ⓥ Serves 2
Takes *20 minutes to prepare + 10 minutes cooling*
4 POINTS *values per recipe*
98 calories *per serving*

goes well after...
The Minestrone Salad on page 149, for an extra 2 POINTS values per serving.

25 g (1 oz) dried tapioca, rinsed
1 x 330 ml can diet cream soda
1 ginger herbal tea bag
100 g (3½ oz) fresh blackberries
1 eating apple, cored and sliced thinly
2 tablespoons low fat fromage frais

1 Put the tapioca, cream soda and tea bag into a small pan. Gently bring to the boil and simmer on a very low heat for 5 minutes. Add the blackberries and simmer for a further 5–10 minutes until cooked. Remove from the heat and leave to cool for 10 minutes.

2 Discard the tea bag, squeezing out the juices and serve the tapioca in bowls, topped with the apple slices and fromage frais.

orange panna cotta

This stunning dessert is smooth and creamy with a real citrus kick. Chill in the fridge for up to 3 days.

Serves 6

Takes *20 minutes to prepare + 45 minutes standing, 3 hours to chill*

11 POINTS *values per recipe*
103 calories *per serving*

goes well after...

The Pot Roast on page 117, for an additional 4 POINTS values per serving.

4 **gelatine leaves**

1 **large orange**

300 ml (10 fl oz) skimmed milk

1 **tablespoon artificial sweetener**

2 **tablespoons orange flower water (optional)**

150 g (5½ oz) low fat soft cheese

2 x 125 g pot low fat Greek style orange yogurt

15–20 **ice cubes**

1 Line 21 cm x 8 cm (8½ inches x 3¼ inches), 1.2 litre (2 pint) loaf tin with clingfilm (it helps to first brush the tin with a little cold water) and put it into the fridge. Put the gelatine leaves into a small bowl and cover with cold water. Set aside.

2 Grate the orange zest finely and put it in a small saucepan. Add the milk and sweetener and bring to a simmer. Remove from the heat. Squeeze the water out of the gelatine leaves and stir the leaves into the warm milk until smooth and melted.

3 Put the orange flower water (if using), soft cheese and yogurt into a jug. Gradually pour the warm milk mixture into the yogurt, beating after each addition until smooth. Put the ice into a large bowl and top up with a little cold water. Stand the jug in the middle of the iced water (this will help chill the mixture) and set aside for 45 minutes, stirring occasionally until it is the thickness of whipped double cream.

4 Meanwhile, cut the top and base off the orange and stand upright on a board. Using a serrated knife, carefully cut away the peel and pith and then cut the orange into thin slices. Remove the loaf tin from the fridge and arrange the orange slices in a row along the base.

5 Pour the thickened milk mixture over the oranges and chill in the fridge for 2–3 hours until set. To serve, upturn on to a serving platter, remove the clingfilm and cut into six slices.

tropical tart

Polenta is a great substitute for pastry, especially when combined with these exotic juicy fruits.

Ⓥ Serves 4

Takes *10 minutes to prepare + 10 minutes cooling + 30 minutes chilling*

8½ POINTS *values per recipe*

121 calories *per serving*

goes well after...

The Skate with Parsley Sauce on page 135, for an extra 5 POINTS values per serving.

200 ml (7 fl oz) skimmed milk

50 g (1¾ oz) quick cook dried polenta

1 teaspoon artificial sweetener

1 teaspoon ground ginger

75 g (2¾ oz) low fat soft cheese

1 x 150 g pot low fat tropical yogurt

2 x 50 g (1¾ oz) fresh pineapple slices**, quartered**

1 ripe kiwi**, peeled, halved and sliced**

150 g (5½ oz) melon slices**, peeled and cut into small pieces**

zest of ½ a lime

1 Pour the milk into a large saucepan and bring it just to the boil. Quickly add the polenta, sweetener and ginger and cook for 1 minute, stirring constantly until cooked. Pour into a 20 cm (8 inch) loose-bottom, round cake tin and level the top with the back of a spoon. Leave to cool for 10 minutes.

2 Meanwhile, mix together the soft cheese and yogurt. Remove the polenta base from the cake tin and slide on to a serving plate. Spread the yogurt mixture over the top of the tart and chill for 30 minutes.

3 Top with the pineapple, kiwi and melon pieces and scatter over the lime zest. Serve immediately.

sparkling fruit jelly

Get your taste buds fizzing with this Black Forest dessert, made with a bottle of sparkling rosé wine.

Serves 6

Takes *10 minutes to prepare + 3 hours chilling*

11 POINTS *values per recipe*

154 calories *per serving*

goes well after...

The Spicy Barley Chicken on page 52, for a great dinner party dessert and an extra 4½ POINTS values per serving.

300 ml (10 fl oz) diet lemonade

2 x 23 g sachets sugar free raspberry jelly

300 g (10½ oz) frozen black forest fruits

1 x 750 ml bottle sparkling rosé wine, such as Lambrusco Rosato

6 tablespoons 0% fat Greek yogurt

1 Put the lemonade into a small saucepan and bring to the boil. Sprinkle over the jelly crystals and whisk until smooth. Set aside.

2 Divide the frozen fruits between six 250 ml (9 fl oz) tall glasses or flutes. Pour the lemonade mixture into a large jug and top up with the sparkling wine, stirring to mix.

3 Divide the lemonade and wine mixture between the glasses and chill for at least 3 hours until set. To serve, top each jelly with a spoonful of yogurt.

Serving suggestion If you are feeling extra indulgent, top the jellies with 1 tablespoon of half fat crème fraîche instead of yogurt, for 3 **POINTS** values per serving.

2 POINTS VALUE

frozen raspberry tiramisu

This Italian favourite will be a sure winner with the family.

Ⓨ ❄ **Serves 8**

Takes *20 minutes to prepare + 15 minutes standing, 4 hours to freeze*

19½ POINTS *values per recipe*

129 calories *per serving*

goes well after...

The Oven Baked Fish and Chips on page 96, for an extra 6 POINTS values per serving.

300 g (10½ oz) reduced fat vanilla ice cream

4 tablespoons instant coffee granules

6 tablespoons boiling water

250 g (9 oz) fresh raspberries

20 sponge fingers (total weight 100 g/3½ oz)

3 tablespoons Belgian chocolate sauce

2 teaspoons cocoa, for dusting

25 g (1 oz) plain chocolate, grated, for dusting

1 Remove the ice cream from the freezer to soften it slightly. Meanwhile, line a 21 cm x 8 cm (8½ inches x 3¼ inches), 1.2 litre (2 pint) loaf tin tightly with enough clingfilm to fold over the top of the tin (brushing the tin with water first will help the clingfilm to stick). In a shallow bowl, mix together the coffee granules and the boiling water until dissolved.

2 Fold the raspberries into the ice cream, squashing the odd one or two. Dip 10 sponge fingers into the coffee mixture, turning until coated, then press into the base of the tin. Spread half the ice cream over the sponge fingers then drizzle with half the chocolate sauce.

3 Dip the remaining sponge fingers in the coffee mixture and arrange in a layer on top of the ice cream. Drizzle with the remaining chocolate sauce and spread over the remaining ice cream. Fold over the clingfilm and freeze for 4 hours until set.

4 To serve, up turn on to a serving plate and remove the clingfilm. Stand for 10–15 minutes then dust the top with cocoa and grated chocolate and slice into eight.

tray bake date scones

The secret to success is to not overwork the mixture - that way you'll get light, well risen scones.

 Makes 9

Takes *15 minutes to prepare, 20 minutes to bake*

22 *POINTS values per recipe*

156 calories *per serving*

goes well after...

The Puffy Pancetta and Leek Omelette on page 38, for an extra 4 POINTS values per serving.

low fat cooking spray

50 g (1¾ oz) low fat polyunsaturated margarine

225 g (8 oz) self raising flour, plus 1 tablespoon for dusting the surface

1 teaspoon bicarbonate of soda

25 g (1 oz) caster sugar

100 g (3½ oz) ready to eat stoned dried dates, chopped finely

1 egg, beaten

50 ml (2 fl oz) skimmed milk

1 teaspoon vanilla extract

1 Preheat the oven to Gas Mark 5/190°C/fan oven 170°C and spray an 18 cm (7 inch) shallow, square baking tin with the cooking spray. In a large bowl, using your fingertips, rub together the margarine and flour until it resembles fine breadcrumbs.

2 Stir in the bicarbonate of soda, sugar, dates, egg, milk and vanilla extract until a soft dough is formed. Try not to over work the mixture, simply stir until all is combined. On a lightly floured surface, roll out the mixture until it is just 2 cm (¾ inch) thick.

3 Stamp out nine scones using a 5 cm (2 inches) round cutter, being careful not to twist the cutter. You will need to re-roll the dough.

4 Transfer to the baking tin, so the scones are lined up next to each other, just touching, and bake in the oven for 15–20 minutes until golden and risen.

apricot surprise pudding

The surprise is that this pud comes with its own zesty sauce at the bottom of the dish.

Ⓥ **Serves 6**
Takes *10 minutes to prepare + standing, 25 minutes to bake*
16 *POINTS* *values per recipe*
172 calories *per serving*

low fat cooking spray
3 eggs, separated
50 g (1¾ oz) caster sugar
50 g (1¾ oz) low fat polyunsaturated margarine
50 g (1¾ oz) self raising flour
zest of a large orange
100 ml (3 fl oz) skimmed milk
1 x 411 g can apricot halves in fruit juice, drained
15 g (½ oz) flaked toasted almonds

1 Preheat the oven to Gas Mark 4/180°C/fan oven 160°C and spray a 1.2 litre (2 pint) ovenproof dish with the cooking spray. In a large bowl, whisk together the egg yolks, sugar and margarine until pale and fluffy. Fold in the flour and orange zest and then gradually stir in the milk to make a smooth batter.

2 In another grease-free, clean bowl, whisk the egg whites until stiff, but not dry peaks. Fold the egg whites into the batter using a large metal spoon, and then pour into the prepared dish. Put the dish into a deep roasting tin.

3 Carefully arrange the apricot halves, cut side down into the batter and scatter over the almonds. Fill the roasting tin with cold water so that it comes halfway up the sides of the dish. Bake in the oven for 25 minutes until risen and firm on top. Leave to stand for 5 minutes, then serve immediately.

spiced pear cake

3 POINTS VALUE

Using grated pears in the mixture helps to keep the cake really moist for up to 1 week, when stored in an airtight container.

Ⓥ Serves 10

Takes *15 minutes to prepare + 10 minutes cooling, 55 minutes to bake*

27½ POINTS *values per recipe*

177 calories *per serving*

goes well after...

The Smoked Chicken Salad on page 33, for an additional 3 *POINTS* values per serving.

low fat cooking spray

3 dessert pears, such as rocha, peeled and cored

juice of a lemon

200 g (7 oz) self raising flour

1 teaspoon baking powder

125 g (4½ oz) caster sugar

1 teaspoon ground mixed spice

50 g (1¾ oz) low fat polyunsaturated margarine, melted

2 eggs, beaten

15 g (½ oz) chopped mixed nuts

1 Preheat the oven to Gas Mark 3/160°C/fan oven 140°C. Spray a non stick 20 cm (8 inch) loose bottom, round cake tin with the cooking spray. Base line with non stick baking parchment. Grate two pears into a bowl and add half the lemon juice.

2 Sift the flour and baking powder into another large mixing bowl and stir in the sugar and mixed spice. Then stir in the grated pears, melted margarine and eggs until well combined.

3 Spoon the mixture into the prepared tin and lightly level the top. Cut the remaining pear into 10 slices. Coat in the remaining lemon juice, then arrange on the top of the cake and sprinkle over the mixed nuts. Bake in the oven for 50–55 minutes until a skewer pushed into the centre of the cake comes out clean.

4 Cool in the tin for 10 minutes. Turn out on to a wire rack. Leave to go cold.

chocolate marshmallow meringue cake

A really indulgent, gooey pudding which will last in the fridge for 2 days.

Serves 6

Takes *20 minutes + cooling, 25 minutes to bake*

20 POINTS *values per recipe*

212 calories *per serving*

low fat cooking spray

3 egg whites

1 teaspoon cream of tartar

150 g (5½ oz) icing sugar, sifted

50 g (1¾ oz) plain flour

25 g (1 oz) cocoa

75 g (2¾ oz) mini marshmallows

75 g (2¾ oz) low fat soft cheese

1 x 90 g pot fat free strawberry fromage frais

175 g (6 oz) strawberries, hulled and quartered

1 Preheat the oven to Gas Mark 3/160°C/fan oven 140°C. Spray a 20 cm (8 inch) loose bottom round cake tin with the cooking spray and line with non stick baking parchment. In a clean, grease-free bowl, whisk the egg whites and cream of tartar until stiff. Continue whisking and add the sifted icing sugar, a third at a time, whisking well after each addition until glossy. Then fold in the flour and cocoa.

2 Spoon into the prepared tin and level the top with a wet spoon. Bake in the oven for 25 minutes. Remove from the oven and press half the marshmallows gently into the surface of the cake at intervals. Return to the oven and bake for 5 minutes. Remove and leave to go cold.

3 To serve, remove from the cake tin and discard the baking parchment. Mix together the soft cheese and fromage frais and spread over the top of the cake. Top with the strawberries and remaining marshmallows. Serve immediately.

Variation Other summer berries will work well such as raspberries, for the same **POINTS** values per serving.

quick banana ice cream

Ⓨ ❋ **Serves 4**
Takes *5 minutes to prepare, 1 hour to freeze*
14 POINTS *values per recipe*
238 calories *per serving*

goes well after...
The Special Pork Chow Mein on page 91, for an extra 4½ POINTS values per serving.

4 bananas (total approximately 900 g/2 lb), peeled
juice of a lime
1 x 200 g pot virtually fat free vanilla yogurt

1 Put the bananas and lime juice in a bowl and mash really well with a fork. Stir in the yogurt and then pour into a shallow baking tray. Freeze for 1 hour or until semi frozen. It should leave a dent when you press it with your finger.

2 Scoop the ice cream into bowls by running the ice cream scoop along the length of the baking tray and serve immediately.

Tip If you are short of space in your freezer, put the banana mixture in a smaller container, but you will need to freeze it for at least 2 hours.

spoil yourself

key lime pie

This is an adaptation of a very famous recipe from Florida where a special variety of limes is used, called Key Limes, hence the name.

Ⓨ Serves 12

Takes *10 minutes + 2 hours chilling*

48 POINTS values per recipe

235 calories *per serving*

200 g (7 oz) light digestive biscuits

1 teaspoon ground ginger

75 g (2¾ oz) low fat polyunsaturated margarine, melted

1 x 405 g can light condensed milk

zest and juice of 4 limes

125 ml (4 fl oz) less than 33% fat double cream

1 x 125 g pot low fat Greek style lemon yogurt

1 Whizz the digestive biscuits and ginger in a food processor, until fine crumbs. Add the melted margarine and whizz again until combined. Press into the base of a 20 cm (8 inch) loose bottomed, fluted tart tin, using your fingers to create a shell up the sides. Chill in the fridge while you do step 2.

2 In a large bowl, whisk the condensed milk, lime zest and juice until thick. Add the cream and yogurt and continue to whisk for 5 minutes until really thick. Spoon the filling on to the base, and create swirls with the back of a spoon.

3 Chill in the fridge for 2 hours until set. To serve, remove from the tin, place on to a serving plate and cut into 12 wedges.

Variation Why not try using lemons instead of limes, for the same **POINTS** values per serving.

whole apple tarts

These individual puddings are so impressive and fuss free. Make them up to 1 day in advance and chill in the fridge until needed.

Serves 4
Takes *15 minutes to prepare + 10 minutes standing, 40 minutes to bake*
18½ POINTS *values per recipe*
270 calories *per serving*

15 g (½ oz) low fat polyunsaturated margarine
50 g (1¾ oz) light muscovado sugar
4 eating apples
30 g (1¼ oz) dried golden sultanas
15 g (½ oz) fresh ginger, peeled and grated
juice of a lemon
125 g (4½ oz) ready rolled puff pastry
1 tablespoon skimmed milk

1 Preheat the oven to Gas Mark 4/180°C/fan oven 160°C. Put the margarine and sugar in a small pan and gently heat until the sugar has dissolved. Bubble for 1 minute. Divide the melted sugar among four 200 ml (7 fl oz) ramekins. Using an apple corer, remove the core from each apple and discard. Carefully slice a little from the bottom of each apple so it stands flat.

2 Put an apple into each ramekin, with the flat bottom upwards. Mix together the sultanas, ginger and lemon juice and use to fill the centre of each apple. Unroll the pastry and lightly roll to make slightly larger. Cut the pastry into four circles, big enough to just cover the top of each ramekin.

3 Cover each ramekin with a circle of pastry and brush the tops with the milk. Bake in the oven for 40 minutes until golden. Remove from the oven and leave to stand for 5–10 minutes.

4 To serve, carefully loosen the pastry from the sides of the ramekin, and upturn on to a plate. Remove the ramekins and serve.

Serving suggestion Serve with 1 tablespoon 0% fat Greek yogurt, for an extra ½ **POINTS** value per serving.

Index by POINTS values